Ailments Through the Ages

By the same author

Ailments Through the Ages

An Alarming History of Famous & Difficult Patients

RICHARD GORDON

Special Edition for PAST TIMES, Oxford, England

First published in Great Britain in 1998
by Michael OMara Books Limited
9 Lion Yard
Tremadoc Road
London SW4 7NQ

A CIP catalogue record for this book is available from the British Library

ISBN 1-85479-367-5

1 3 5 7 9 10 8 6 4 2

Typeset by ensystems

Printed and bound by WSOY, Finland

Contents

THE ARTS

DOCTORS AND NURSES

THE COMMON PEOPLE

FICTION

$\mathcal{R}$ULERS

GEORGE WASHINGTON

1732–1799

GEORGE WASHINGTON had difficult teeth.

The mouth that could not tell a lie suffered savage revenge under the tormenting pitchforks of the dental devils. When he was twenty-two, fighting the French at Fort Duquesne, his teeth began to drop out. He fought the British from 1775 with constant toothache, a distraction surely worse than Napoleon's prolapsed piles at Waterloo. He conscientiously cleaned his teeth with sponges and scrapers, but they rotted and wobbled and demanded pulling, until in 1796 he lost his last—a lower premolar—into the eventual care of the New York Academy of Medicine, where it is fittingly gold-cased.

Washington ended the Revolutionary War with several intrusive teeth fixed to his surviving ones with wire, which he tightened up with pincers. His first full set of teeth was fixed to plates of lead alloy coated with beeswax (with the alarming unrecognised hazard of lead poisoning). The set weighed three ounces, the equivalent of carrying your loose change in your mouth instead of your pocket.

Washington filed down the metal bases repeatedly for comfort, so the teeth worked themselves forward in his mouth. It 'gives the lips the pointing and swelling appearance,' he complained to his favoured dentist John Greenwood in December 1798. 'It will have the effect of forcing the lip out just under the nose.' Dr Greenwood of New York charged $15 a set, was to be found fourth door down from the theatre towards St Paul's Church, advertised himself as 'Dentist to the President George Washington', and quoted him: 'I shall always prefer your services to that of any other in the line of your present profession.' Martha Washington also had false teeth, at $28 a set, but they broke in her mouth and took two years to repair.

The difficulties of retaining such apparatus in your mouth, without protruding your upper jaw like a rabbit or your lower like Popeye, were worsened by the pair of coiled steel springs looped on each side to keep the upper and lower sets apart. The normal position which these springs created for the teeth was that of hilarious laughter or screeching pain. To keep the teeth together when displayed outside the mouth required several twists of wire. Inside, it demanded an exertion of the facial muscles that struck an English visitor in 1790: 'His mouth was like no other I ever saw; the lips firm and the under jaw seemed to grasp the upper with force, as if the muscles were in full action when he sat still'—a valuable impression of the iron determination of the American President towards his vanquished overlords. Another Englishman calling on the President for breakfast (sliced tongue and bread and butter) took the more optimistic view of 'a certain anxiety visible in his countenance, with marks of extreme sensibility.'

At a Washington banquet: 'The President seemed to bear in his countenance a settled aspect of melancholy. No cheering ray of sunshine broke through the cloudy gloom of settled seriousness.' Unlike President Coolidge, he was not missing the jokes, he was trying to keep his mouth shut. He could have relished the feast had he first placed his teeth beside his plate, a gesture of similarly equipped guests who wore false teeth for appearance and articulation, not mastication. But Washington did not care for the unappetising habit. Though he followed the custom of keeping his teeth overnight in port, because otherwise they tasted vile; his dentist objected that this removed the polish and advised beer instead. Between courses, Washington indulged his inclination for banging on the table with his knife and fork. His most comfortable eating was pickled tripe, dispatched to his order across the Atlantic from the bespoke grocers of London.

Washington's teeth in his sixties were of ivory pegged into gold (which in humbler mouths were useful for the pawnshop) They still worked forward into an ungracious pout, which Gilbert Stuart remedied for the President's portrait of 1796 by inserting cotton rolls into his sitter's mouth. This gave his lower face the sagging puffiness of our senile Queen Victoria. Which is sad, because this likeness of the President is the most cherished, appearing on the dollar bill.

At the end of the eighteenth century, dental transplants were as popular as today's cardiac ones. Laughing gas being half a century ahead, they were painful oral expressions of class distinction. The fashionable lady with toothache endured an extraction simultaneously with the errand boy or serving girl, the youngster's healthy fang in her mouth being exchanged for coins from her purse. (In New York, you could get two guineas a tooth, but front only.)

In 1777, sixteen-year-old Amy Lyon from Scotland, who had not lasted as a nursemaid to a London doctor, was en route to the dentist's desperate to relieve her destitution by volunteering as a mass tooth donor, when she was luckily picked up by Captain Payne of the Royal Navy and, after having his baby, and acting a Goddess at James Graham's Temple of Health in Pall Mall, and renaming herself Emma, and becoming mistress of Sir Harry Fetherstonhaugh of Sussex, who passed her on to the Hon Charles Greville MP, and becoming wife of Sir William Hamilton, in 1793 she bit Horatio Nelson.

There was a painless transplant, from dead young men. The Resurrectionists were already digging in churchyards by moonlight, and in the next century 'Waterloo Teeth' offered a rich gleaning from the field of Napoleon's defeat. In the American Civil War, dental pirates with pincers were snapping on the heels of the army, their loot packed in barrels and exported to England, where you could buy their plunder respectably by mail order.

The pathos of an Englishman with the tooth of an unknown American soldier in his mouth is balanced by the honour bestowed on the anonymous donors of Washington's first lower set. To chew for the first President of the United States is a distinction dwarfing the toiling of the builders of the Pyramids.

Washington's dentist, Dr Greenwood, had advertised in the papers teeth adapted from the tusks of the walrus, 'the enamel of which is much thicker than the human teeth and so hard as to

5

produce fire equal to a flint, and so light the color, that when formed into the shape of human teeth, they cannot be perceived from them by the most strict observer.' Washington's upper teeth were from an elk. The European 'elk' is the ungainly American moose, but the American elk is the wapiti, a springing red deer with big antlers. Just the animal to give élan to the dreariest menus and conversations!

> *For there was never yet philosopher*
> *That could endure the toothache patiently,*

observed Leonato in *Much Ado about Nothing*. Washington endured false teeth more philosophically than toothache, but found that they made him mumble, which turned him from public speaking. His sixth successor, Andrew Jackson, refused to wear his brand new set because they were too uncomfortable, and made as few speeches as possible. The advance of dentistry is magnificent, but how sad that it liberated the oratory of a politician with comparably awful dentition, Adolf Hitler.

$\mathcal{N}$APOLEON

1769–1821

'$\mathcal{M}$EDICINE is the science of murderers,' Napoleon told his Physician-in-Chief, Baron René Desgenettes.

The doctor replied: 'How would you define the science of conquerors?'

Touché impérial.

In his twenty years of campaigning for the subjection of Europe and the Middle East, Napoleon was wounded only once.

On 6 July, 1798, ten days after taking Alexandria, his three divisions mustering 10,000 men started marching across the desert to conquer Cairo. They had neither food nor water, Napoleon having overlooked that in the Egyptian desert in midsummer they would be unable as usual to live off the land.

> Never had an army experienced such great hardships and such acute privations. Scorched by the rays of a merciless sun, we marched on foot for mile after endless mile across the burning sand amid unrelieved desolation. Only with difficulty were we able to find a little stagnant water in pools that were scarcely liquid. Parched with thirst and overcome by the heat, the strongest soldiers collapsed under the weight of their equipment,

wrote Surgeon-in-Chief Baron Dominique-Jean Larrey, whose only resource was the distribution of sips of brandy-and-water from his accustomed leather bottle. Equally alarmingly, the troops were beginning to see mirages.

Four days' march brought them to the run-down village of

Damanhur, a quarter of their way. The Surgeon-in-Chief was summoned urgently. Napoleon had been kicked on the right knee by his Arab horse. Baron Larrey let blood with a small incision into the puffy bruise obscuring the patella, applied a dressing, advised rest and prayed.Ten days later, they reached the Pyramids and the wound had healed. On 24 July, Napoleon triumphantly entered Cairo, but on 1 August Nelson did for him in the battle of the Nile.

Diseases with which Napoleon has been inflicted by historians:

amoebic abscess	malaria
arsenic poisoning	manic-depressive psychosis
bladder stones	neurotic dermatitis
brucellosis	obesity
cancer of the stomach	peptic ulcer
cholera	pituitary deficiency
dysentery	syphilis
epilepsy	tuberculosis
haemorrhoids	varicose veins
hypogonadism	Zollinger-Ellison syndrome (too much gastric juice).

Had Napoleon chosen even sparingly of this pathological menu, his plight would have worsened from the Revolutionary reorganisation of France's medical education. The National Convention's decree of 12 August 1792 abolished the thirty-three French medical schools as septic foci of privilege. As France had been at war against the Prussians since April, and many of the army's 1,500 medical officers were already dead from shot or disease, these were replenished by conscription of all French doctors under forty. As they, too, ran out, medical schools were hastily established in military hospitals. 'Schools of Health' were founded in 1794 to provide crash courses in medicine, though their qualifying licences were readily available for cash. When Napoleon took command of the army in italy in 1796, his medical services were lethal.

Napoleon acknowledged doctors only as part of the military machine. And reluctantly, because army wisdom was 'that the sick and wounded cease to be men when they can no longer be soldiers'.

He was luckily served by the resourceful and ingenious Larrey, an ex-Naval surgeon off the frigate *Vigilante*, a graduate of the Hôtel Dieu in Paris, who aged thirty was posted to Italy from the chair of anatomy at the new Ecole de Médicine Militaire at Val-de-Grâce. He invented the ambulance.

The wounded had previously been left on the battlefield until the fighting had swept one way or the other, when they could be tended or collected in carts, the only relief of their suffering meanwhile being death. Larrey's two-horse *ambulances volantes*, nothing but a pair of large wheels, a long shaft, sound springs and a two-man-sized box, could gallop into battle like the guns of the flying artillery and hastily evacuate the casualties to safety. Larrey and his medical officers manned the machines, risking their lives to dress wounds where they had been inflicted. Soon there were hundreds of heartening ambulances behind the French lines, also a four-wheeled model, and a six-horse version with eight surgeons sitting in each others' laps to tend a thousand casualties, and for the Egyptian campaign panniers astride the humps of camels. Wellington would have nothing of the idea; ambulances would only get in the way behind the lines and collide with the guns.

The surgery of the times instructed Larrey's skill as an amputator: 200 a day at Borodino. It was the only treatment for severe wounds or compound fractures, to be performed promptly, sometimes in the open, sometimes when 'it was so cold that it froze the urine in my chamber-pot', often under fire. Larrey was the first surgeon to risk cutting off a leg at the hip, though he quailed after six. He joined sixty battles and 400 skirmishes and was wounded thrice. Such devotion to the Grande Armée won the acclamation of both its ranks and its commander, who in 1799 presented him with a sword of honour inscribed *Aboukir et Larrey* (there had been 1,900 casualties).

'Have you dared to kill officers' horses to feed your wounded?' Napoleon once asked Larrey sternly.

'Yes.' Rations were low, and Larrey had concocted a *bouillon de viande extemporané*.

'Well, I will make you Baron of the Empire,' Napoleon said, expressing his invaluable appreciation of efficiency.

'Larrey, the most virtuous man I have ever known,' the Emperor finally assessed in his will, backing the compliment with a bequest of 100,000 francs. Patients of substance often make welcome postmortem gifts to those who have guided their trek to the grave. But even the grateful patient can turn difficult.

After the retreat from Moscow, Czar Alexander I pursued Napoleon into Germany, but in May 1813 was beaten in the battle of Lützen, south of Leipzig. The miserable remnants of the Grande Armée had been patched from Paris with youthful recruits, whose officers furiously suspected them of enduring self-inflicted wounds to escape the slaughter. Three thousand young soldiers had been found wounded in the hand or forearm, their blackened sleeves and skin indicating a close musket shot. With a vindictiveness which characterised Europe's conquerors of the following century, forty-eight soldiers—four from each corps—were selected to be shot. Larrey objected.

Napoleon was furious. He ordered Larrey to convene a court of enquiry to examine the suspects. Larrey ascribed the wounds to incompetent and hasty arms drill. The two rear ranks had been shooting at the front one. Napoleon refused to believe him. Larrey flourished his surgical notes: most of the condemned men had other wounds elsewhere. Napoleon jumped up and down. He gave in. That night, unlike Hitler, he reflected on his wicked ruthlessness and remorsefully sent Larrey his portrait, in a diamond-encrusted frame.

By February 1799, Napoleon was on his way home from Egypt via Asia Minor. He had intended to incite a revolution in Syria, overthrow the Turks, and march triumphantly to Paris through the Ottoman Empire. But a British squadron from Constantinople under Sir Sidney Smith, who had burnt the French fleet in Toulon in 1793, frustrated the venture at Acre and obliged Napoleon's reverse to the Pyramids.

In March, the army of 12,000 men ran into the plague at Jaffa. Napoleon had just shot 2,500 prisoners of war there: they were reducing the meagre French rations, and escorting them back to Egypt would dangerously weaken the French army. Baron Larrey agreed wholeheartedly with this logic.

Larrey did not agree with Napoleon about the plague. Bubonic plague is conveyed by fleas from dead rats, it is the illness memorialized as the Great Plague of London and the Black Death. Napoleon decreed that it was non-contagious. The bursting buboes in moribund groins he believed to indicate some uninfectious fever that afflicted only the uncourageous and irresolute. Anyway, that was the line to keep up morale. The troops were becoming terrified.

Physician-in-Chief Baron Desgenettes courted Napoleonic favour by demonstrating the General to be absolutely right, pricking his own groins with a knife point of bubonic pus. Napoleon inspected a Jaffa mosque commandeered as a hospital, shifted a corpse, even felt a bubo: had a rat-flea got him, it would have spared Europe fifteen years of systematic bloodshed.

Physically, Napoleon presented few difficulties for his doctors. In middle age he developed an *embonpoint*. He had a horror of surgery. The night before the Battle of Borodino he had trouble urinating, from small stones in the bladder. At Fontainebleau en route for Elba he attempted suicide with opium, but the faint-hearted dosage only made him sick. At Waterloo, he was incommoded with prolapsed piles, hardly the strategical equivalent of Nelson's blind eye at Copenhagen.

When he was piped aboard the *Bellerophon* at Rochefort at ten in the morning of 15 July 1815, Napoleon had already introduced himself to the Prince Regent: 'I come, like Themistocles, to seat myself at the hearth of the British people.' He anticipated his captors being terribly decent and inviting him to end his turbulent days in the easygoing comfort of an English country gentleman in Berkshire, for which he had already the sobriquet 'Colonel Muiron'. But the fire in the hearth had gone out. More suspicious, after Elba, than Themistocles' host Admetus in 470 BC, the British decided, as the alternative to hanging him, upon Cold Comfort Farm in St Helena. Wooden, poky, gloomy, damp, single-storey, mud-invested Longwood House was Napoleon's quenching end, though it provided a billiard-room to pass his long evenings.

Napoleon's doctor on St Helena was another Corsican, Francesco Antommarchi, an anatomist from Pisa who had been selected by the patient's mother. He did not enjoy much confidence as a healer: 'I would give him my horse to dissect, but I would not trust him with the cure of my own foot.' In 1817, Napoleon suffered a painful swelling on the right of his abdomen; that winter he developed right shoulder pain and dizziness; by the summer of 1820 he had nausea which worsened into anorexia, then violent vomiting, haematemesis, dyspnoea and finally an irregular pulse, clamminess and death on 5 May 1821. The billiard-room suggested itself for the post-mortem, at last invoking the expertise of Dr Antommarchi. The British sent along seven doctors to see fair play. They all agreed that he died from cancer of the stomach, though everyone in Napoleon's sadly tattered court knew that he had been poisoned. The corpse himself had no doubts: 'My death is premature. I have been assassinated by the English oligarchy,' he accused in his will.

A hundred and fifty years later, a specimen of Napoleon's hair was discovered in Glasgow to contain sixty times the normal content of arsenic. In 1980, a souvenir scrap of flock wallpaper from Napoleon's bedroom was found by spectroscopy to contain enough arsenic to emit, under the influence of the indigenous damp and moulds of Longwood House, enough arsenic gas to cause symptoms of poisoning. So perhaps he was assassinated by his wallpaper. The next distinguished sufferer from these noxious vapours was Clare Luce, the playwright of *Kiss the Boys Goodbye* and editor of *Vanity Fair*, who became American Ambassador to Rome in 1953 but, unlike the Emperor of France, could command in her exile her bedroom being rehung.

ITLER

1889–1945

ADOLF HITLER'S foremost difficulty as a patient was his refusal to take his clothes off.

The opening episode of the Hitler medical testament was on 13 October 1918, when he faced British gas shells at Ypres.

> As early as midnight, a number of us passed out, a few of our comrades forever. Towards morning I, too, was seized with pain and grew worse with every quarter hour, and at seven in the morning I stumbled and tottered back with burning eyes; taking with me my last report of the War. A few hours later, my eyes had turned into glowing coals; it had grown dark around me . . .

he remembered vividly in *Mein Kampf* fifteen years later.

Hitler ended the war in hospital in Pomerania, a peaceful spot on the far side of Germany.

Professor Wilmanns, chief military psychiatrist for the State of Baden and later head of psychiatry at Heidelberg, suggested that Corporal Hitler was affected not by gas but by hysterical blindness after a close shell-burst: shortly afterwards, the corporal had seen the Virgin Mary and was placed under arrest. An unchivalrous diagnosis, but anyway Hitler was already developing into a literally screaming neurotic.

A shrapnel wound on the left thigh, suffered on 7 October 1915 on the Somme, was recorded for history when Hitler was compelled to denude himself in a Munich jail in November 1923. He weighed seventy-six kilograms, and had a mildly raised blood pressure of 143/90, but it went up to 200 when he got excited. He had only a right testicle. He suffered a post-nasal drip, boils on the back of his neck and eczema on his left shin. His teeth were dreadful, through a lifetime of shirking dentists. Later omnipotence enabled these teeth to be beautifully engineered in gold, and they are his only memorial: utilised by the Russians to identify his body, they may be viewed in a jar in Moscow. 'Psychiatric condition: Normal', the Munich prison doctor added.

Hitler was awaiting trial for high treason. His offence was the fiasco of the Beer Hall Putsch, which left nineteen dead on the pavement outside the Munich Feldherrnhalle. He was found guilty, but six months seemed to the court a reasonable sentence, and nine years later he was ruling Germany.

A dictator's health risks the health of his country. And a dictator, being above human failings, can never be visibly ill. Such difficulties for his doctors were augmented by Hitler's refusal to be x-rayed, even with all his clothes on. Why should any German see through the Führer, when the statesmen of Europe could not?

Radiography was necessitated by Hitler's appointment as Chancellor in 1933 coinciding with severe abdominal pain after eating, perhaps from a stomach ulcer. He belched often, a potential disaster for his speeches. Like many less dictatorial patients, he decided that he knew better than his doctors and prescribed himself a diet of rusks, yogurt, honey and mushrooms, and turned to Dr Koester's Antigas Pills, which he swore by, and continued to ingest through the war. The prescribed dose of two pills before meals was innocuous, but refusing to be dictated to by pharmacists Hitler swallowed them by the handful, inviting poisoning by their ingredients of atropine and strychnine.

In 1935, after triumphantly restoring Saarland to Germany, Hitler developed a polyp on his right vocal cord. This had a fearsome precedent. The Emperor Frederick III had died in 1888 of a malignant laryngeal growth, in the hands of Queen Victoria's throat surgeon, flashy Sir Morell Mackenzie. Hitler's polyp was benign, but it gave him a squawky voice. Had he balked at the surgical recommendation for its removal, the world would have been saved much trouble: the speeches which mesmerised and moved Europe could hardly have been so effective if delivered in the tones of Donald Duck.

His mid-forties presented another difficulty for his doctors. The superhuman do not wear glasses, even for reading in bed. But even eyes which flash inspiration to the masses and pierce the wicked hearts of their enemies inescapably develop presbyopia, and are obliged to find how far down they can read on an optician's wall chart. Hitler perched above his moustache a pair of steel-rimmed glasses, afterwards the more fashionable horned-rimmed bifocals, for signing his horrifying decrees. Their existence was as close a state secret as the door connecting his own bedroom to Eva Braun's. So was the *Führerschrift*, the typescript of his fearsome speeches in letters as big as a child's reading-book. Photographs which caught Hitler in glasses were instantly destroyed, while Churchill and Roosevelt appeared unconcerned at viewing the cataclysmic world mildly through their half-moons and pince-nez.

Hitler was otherwise pretty healthy. He was a fanatical non-smoker a generation too soon, and drank sparingly his country's delightful beer. He bit the skin round his thumbnails and his first two fingernails, the more intensely the more excited he became. He caught infective jaundice in 1944, like many people on both sides during the war. His electrocardiogram in 1944 indicated impaired coronary blood-flow and high blood pressure, like many other men of fifty-five. He developed a tremor of his left arm, but that was during Stalingrad and El Alamein. He suffered ruptured eardrums and minor burns when his officers tried to blow him to bits in his Wolf's Lair headquarters on the Russian front in 1944— the only practical anti-Nazi resistance, for which they were hanged with piano-wire.

One of these burns turned septic, and was treated successfully with the invention of Professor Florey of Oxford, penicillin, which the Afrika Corps had captured and was being produced from its mould as urgently in Germany as in the brewery vats of America. Hitler was in normal health, if psychologically depressed, when he married Eva Braun, the next day threw a champagne lunch, then killed the pair of them with cyanide. He also killed his dog Blondi:

suspicious of pharmacy to the last, Hitler wanted to make sure that the glass capsules worked.

The difficulties that Hitler created for his doctors had by then become deadly.

When Hitler took power, the young and handsome Dr Karl Brandt travelled with him everywhere as a surgical precaution, and was shortly reinforced by Dr Hans Karl von Hasselbach. In 1936, both were overshadowed by the massive Dr Theo Morell, aged forty-nine, moon-faced, hair plastered over bald dome, three heavy gold rings on his left fingers, a former doctor on ocean liners who became a fashionable practitioner in the Kurfürstendamm in Berlin. His specialty was sexual and psychological disorders. He was a comparatively unintelligent professional nonentity, who became a medical Rasputin.

Morell was recommended to Hitler by his photographer Heinrich Hoffmann in 1935. Hitler's enthusiastic response to his first consultation was: 'Nobody has ever before told me so clearly and precisely what is wrong with me. His method of cure is so logical that I have the greatest confidence in him. I shall follow his prescriptions to the letter.' Morell briskly goose-stepped into Hitler's intimate circle. Hitler forbade any criticism of him. The dictator called often at Morell's country home on Schwanenwerder Island for tea, and he loved Frau Morell's almond cakes. He pressed his henchmen, who despised and laughed at the fat doctor, to consult him for even trivial ailments. Foreign Minister von Ribbentrop and the ruler of Eastern Europe, Rosenberg, (we hanged both later) became his patients, like Goebbels and architect Speer. Rudolf Hess flew to Scotland in 1941 fortified with a packet of Morell's vitamin tablets in his flying-jacket. At Munich in September 1938 Morell treated Mr Neville Chamberlain for flu.

Morell's success was in perfecting a bedside manner towards rich, important and idolised people. His clinical technique was to exaggerate a patient's imagined illness, treat it with useless drugs and glow in the cure. Anyone truly sick he sagely referred to someone who knew something about it. So persuasive was Morell's professional personality that Hitler stripped off and permitted a complete examination, down to per rectum. 'His psychic state was very complex,' Morell recalled.

Hitler was continuing to suffer stomach pains and lack of appetite. Morell diagnosed exhaustion of the intestinal flora, whatever that means. The cure would take a year. Hitler was elated. 'What luck that I met Morell!' he was shortly proclaiming round the Nazi Olympus. 'He has saved my life. Wonderful, the way he has helped me! I could no longer live without him.'

Hitler enthusiastically swallowed red capsules filled with vigorous living bacteria, which would overwhelm the deficient, clapped-out ones in his gut and acclaim victory over his dyspepsia. The blitzkrieg was so successful that he conscientiously took two capsules daily, from the reoccupation of the Rhineland until D-day. As the encapsulated germs were all descended from those discovered in the faeces of a Bulgarian peasant, this was the only democratic gesture that Hitler ever made.

Of passing interest, Hitler's faeces on 2 June 1943 'had a bright brownish colour and showed a rich dash of gall-coloured partly emulsified oil (laxative)'. He took laxatives lavishly, sucked caffeine-containing hard candy, and gave himself camomile enemas locked in the loo. It was all to lose weight: a mystical German leader cannot be pot-bellied. He bought patent medicines so extravagantly that his chauffeur had to pack a bag of them for travelling.

Morell was himself an exponent of blunderbuss therapy. He gave Hitler almost a hundred different remedies of varying effectiveness, usually by injection—'Herr Reich Injection Master,' Göring addressed Morell, to his offence. The prescriptions were mostly innocuous: vitamins, hormones, phosphorous, dextrose, glucose, useless cold cures, and extracts of the testis and seminal vesicles from young bulls to cheer him up. He also applied leeches. He would have liked to apply soothing massage, but the prospect was as fantastic as Siegfried being massaged by the Rhine Maidens.

Like everyone round Hitler, Morell had a uniform: grey, with Hippocratic snakes on the collar, as presented by doctors on either side in the war. But he held no rank in the Nazi Party, and envied the smart black and silver uniforms of SS colonels Brandt and von Hasselbach.

In 1944, the other doctors ganged up on Morell over his secret administration to Hitler of Dr Koester's Antigas pills. Dr Giesing, called in because of Hitler's exploded eardrums, discovered six mysterious black pills on Hitler's breakfast-tray. He identified them by plundering Morell's drug cupboard, and as Hitler was suffering also from jaundice he made a brilliant diagnosis of strychnine poisoning. This would be disproved by any medical textbook, but the Führer's doctors did not feel any need of one. The three doctors denounced Morell for treating their patient behind their backs, and a terrifying meeting was held in the presence of Himmler. But Hitler brushed the charges away, declaiming that he had taken Dr Koester's pills long before meeting Morell. Adding that he had no time for disagreeing doctors, he fired the three accusers.

From 1941, every morning before Hitler rose from his bed, Morell gave an injection to make him feel fresh, alert, and ready for the problems of the day. After 1943, every second afternoon the Führer dropped his brown trousers for Morell to inject into his gluteal muscles a mixture of vitamins—to which he had the clinical inspiration of adding the addictive stimulant amphetamine. 'Speed' or 'ecstasy' to its fans, amphetamine stimulates the sympathetic nervous system, increases the pulse, diminishes the appetite, excites and elates. People began to notice how, immediately after Morell's consultations, Hitler became alert, cheerful and talkative. 'I was completely exhausted and after his injection I felt fresh again,' Hitler testified to Mussolini in 1944.

The injections increased as the war worsened. The trousers were being dropped five times daily, and the dose rose eightfold. The top Nazis became curious about what he was getting. Morell kept the remedy secret: 'The Fuhrer's special mixture.' Hitler liked his hard drugs. Dr Giesing had used cocaine as a local anaesthetic before swilling his sinuses: Hitler so enjoyed the treatment he demanded it repeatedly. He had his regular eye-drops increased from six to thirteen: they contained cocaine.

Hitler paid Morell total fees of 360,000 Reichsmarks (in 1939, that was £17,647 or $86,470). His assessment of his doctor's scientific intellect is measurable by his gift to Morell in 1944 of an electron microscope, of which only four had been made in Germany. Morell would have been bemused about what to use it for, or even how to work it. He installed it distantly at the health resort of Bad Reichenhall, near the Austrian frontier, and forgot about it.

On 23 April 1945, Morell abandoned the lethally chaotic Berlin bunker and his patient, who by then was threatening to have him shot. Morell awarded his practice to Dr Stumpfegger, joined a planeload of scampering Nazis bound for Munich, and was reunited with his electron microscope by entering hospital at Bad Reichenhall. He was picked up by the Americans in July 1945 and imprisoned at Dachau, sharing a cell with Dr Brandt.

All Hitler's doctors were interrogated at the Military Intelligence Service Center, the 'Ashcan'. Morell was released in 1947 and died from heart disease in 1948. Dr Stumpfegger was killed in Berlin. Dr Giesing and Dr von Hasslebach resumed practice. Dr Brandt, as Reich Commissioner for sanitation and health, had been arrested by Hitler on 16 April 1945, for defying his orders by moving his family from Berlin westwards towards the advancing Americans, prospectively more merciful than the Russians. He was sentenced to be hanged, but execution was delayed from day to day, he was released after Hitler's death, tried by the War Crimes Tribunal for medical experiments in concentration camps, and in 1947 it was the Americans who hanged him.

CHURCHILL

1874–1965

I<small>N THE SUMMER</small> of 1947 we were still clearing up from the War. My hospital, St Bartholomew's, was fossilized in its bomb-damage. The dense City of London separating it from St Paul's was sweepingly flat, pretty with tufts of grass and rosebay willowherb. We lingered fifteen miles away in the Hertfordshire countryside, in a sprawling, red-brick, slate-roofed Victorian lunatic asylum, where 'Bart's' had been evacuated, as had the other traditional London hospitals, in 1939.

Blitz casualties had arrived in converted London buses. Service casualties reached our specialist units from the battlefields of the world, and we flowed with the daily tides of civilian patients. All was improvised: the operating theatres were partitioned in a lofty gymnasium, with cats to be discovered warming themselves among the steam sterilisers, and bats flitted along the endless corridor connecting the blocks of two-storey blacked-out wards, all without lifts. It taught me that the architecture of any hospital is only as magnificent as the abilities of its staff.

One morning that June, when I was a young doctor administering anaesthetics, a pleasant-looking grey-haired visitor appeared in our operating theatre corridor, accompanying the professor of surgery. A nurse whispered that he was Sir Thomas Dunhill, KCVO, CMG, Sergeant Surgeon to the reigning King George VI and former Surgeon to King George V, now retired from Bart's and aged seventy-one. Sir Thomas specialised in removal of the thyroid gland, which he had practised in his native Australia on goats. To our surprise, he shortly scrubbed-up and assisted the professor with the repair of an inguinal hernia. I was flummoxed.

Why was the King's surgeon—or even the professor—performing an operation of such boring straightforwardness it was usually left to the juniors? Sir Thomas repaired all the hospital's hernias for a week. I hazarded that he had missed out on hernias while he was busy operating on goats.

On 12 June, the newspapers announced that Winston Churchill's right inguinal hernia had been repaired by Sir Thomas Dunhill. I wondered if the half-dozen men nursing their fresh scars suspected that they had been guinea-pigs in the national interest.

Churchill was seventy-two, had sustained the hernia for two years, had tried controlling it with an old-fashioned truss, but suffered skin irritation and a melancholy contemplation that the sack holding his vital organs was bursting open. He had prepared himself for the operation by cutting down his cigars by half for a fortnight. A herniorrhaphy usually took about fifteen minutes, but it took Sir Thomas over two hours. When Sir Thomas attended him again six years later, after he had badly burnt his hand by exploding a match-box with his cigar, this time Churchill insisted on applying the treatment of gauze dressings himself.

The selection of Sir Thomas, instead of some young general surgeon with hernias at his fingertips, seemed impelled by the concept that no person could lay hands on the patient without a title and royal connections. The choice was made by Lord Moran, Churchill's personal physician, President of the Royal College of Physicians and a vigorous medical politician, known in the profession as 'Corkscrew Charlie'.

Whatever Lord Moran's clinical snobberies, he had the guile to manage for twenty-five years a patient who saw all doctors as fumbling servants, flunkies with the habit of idly observing the natural progress of his diseases instead of instantly restoring him to globally essential activity. 'No intelligent man, properly handled, can ever be a bad patient', Moran had determined steelily. The cleverest doctors can be simple souls away from the bedside, but Lord Moran had a way with him among men of power—like Lord Dawson of Penn, who provided stealthy euthanasia for King George V in 1936, and won instant promotion to a Viscount. Moran made a reliably submissive confessor: 'You have more influence with him than anyone,' he was told, 'but of course that's not very much.'

Churchill took intense interest in his pulse-rate and temperature, he questioned his medical attendants closely on the mechanism of their blood-counts and x-rays, and he demanded immediate explanation of his symptoms. After scraping a win in the 1951 election, he became deaf. He flouted Moran's recommendation and summoned an ear, nose and throat surgeon who magically sprayed his throat before speeches (if only with salt and water) and who busily syringed his ears (though they were waxless). Churchill liked a doctor who *did* something. He hence liked flashy nostrums and quacks.

The man in bed remained the man in charge. In Tunis during his Middle East expedition in 1943, Churchill developed pneumonia and fibrillation of the heart. The sulpha drugs (discovered in Hitler's Germany) saved his life, but when two London professors whom Moran had called to his elbow advised a fortnight's rest in bed:

> Winston suddenly became red in the face with rage.
> 'Why,' he growled, 'a fortnight?'
> They replied vaguely that he might get a relapse.
> 'Have you,' he said angrily, 'in the course of your long experience ever seen a patient get a second attack of pneumonia through getting about too early?'
> Rather cowed by his violence, they admitted that they had not.

In 1946, Alexander Fleming was summoned to the infected eyes which were rendering Churchill petulant; but discovering a staphylococcus in Churchill's nose resistant to penicillin, he became more interested in the unruly organism than the domineering patient.

While Churchill was well, he saw no reason to fuss about the time when he might not be. It is consoling to a generation chastened by calories that after an all-night sitting of Parliament he ate a good English breakfast topped by his first whisky-and-soda of the day (this generally arrived while he was shaving). He drank champagne as he felt like it and smoked cigars uncaringly—once, while using a hissing oxygen mask in his RAF transport plane, he nearly outdid the *Luftwaffe* by bringing himself down in flames. On his wartime missions to Italy and the Middle East he refused to swallow mepacrine tablets (another bestowal of Nazi Germany) to prevent malaria: he declared that they made him ill, they made everyone who took them turn yellow as though dying, and they were anyway unnecessary. Moran objected. Churchill telephoned George VI in Buckingham Palace, and informed Moran that *the King* had not taken mepacrine when abroad. So there!

Since becoming an MP at the beginning of the century, Churchill suffered from periodic depression, from anxiety, and from the uncertainty that haunts successful men and goads them to perfection. His 'Black Dog' sniffed at his heels for months on end. He dreaded his mind going blank, breaking down—it would be for a second time—into humiliating silence in the House. He disliked visiting hospitals: too depressing. Or looking over the side of ships: too suicidal. Or psychiatrists: they produced insulin coma, which might be eternal.

Churchill's bedside table was loaded with medicines, patent medicines and quack medicines. He took his nightly sleeping pills washed down with whisky, applied ointment in his nostrils and drops to his eyes, his valet rubbed his back with calamine, he swallowed a bowl of soup, directed a jet of water to swill the corners of his mouth, brushed his hair carefully and went to bed. Oddities are the inheritance of all mankind. He also suffered from occasional indigestion which he ascribed to painting, and he took two steaming baths a day.

When he turned eighty, his medical history offered a coronary thrombosis, three attacks of pneumonia, the hernia operation and two strokes. And a senile itch, for which he tried fourteen ointments and lotions. He was still Prime Minister.

One stroke had come in Monte Carlo in 1949, the next followed an impromptu speech at a Downing Street dinner for the Italian Prime Minister in the summer of 1953. The occupational threat presented by the latest stroke ensured that the illness was desperately kept from the Press by a Downing Street conspiracy enthusiastically joined by Lord Moran, who had long considered himself less a court physician than a pivotal member of the Government. He prepared a bland bulletin about 'arduous duties' and 'disturbance of the cerebral circulation, resulting in attacks of giddiness', and advised substituting Churchill's imminent journey to meet President Eisenhower in Bermuda with a month's rest. It was not bland enough for Churchill's henchmen, R. A. Butler and Lord Salisbury, who changed it to *very* arduous duties requiring lightening for a month. Lord Moran read this, fervently hoping that the patient would not die overnight and make them look fools.

Gladstone had been Prime Minister aged eighty-four, but there were indications that the statesman who had saved the nation should now save himself from the exertions of politics. In 1954, Malcolm Muggeridge's *Punch* ran a cartoon of a corpse-faced Churchill at his desk with unlit cigar and unopened red boxes, captioned from Psalm 104: *Man goeth forth to his work, and to his labour: until the evening. Punch* lost valuable, frothing subscribers, but it had illustrated the national chatter. Only Harold Macmillan (the next Prime Minister but one) dared relay this to the old man.

In April 1955, Churchill reluctantly resigned, and reluctantly lived another ten years. That summer, his memory was fading, his words were dribbling, his mind was confused, he forgot the name of Anthony Eden (the next Prime Minister).

As the years went by he gave up reading. He seldom spoke, and when he did it was difficult to follow what he said. He did not seem to know his friends. We would rise to our feet as he came into the room, supported under the arms by his nurses. As they pushed him to his chair his feet made a slapping sound on the floor. Very small, almost shrunken, he appeared huddled up in the depths of a big chair. There he sat through the afternoon hours, staring into the fire, giving it a prod with his stick when the room felt cold.

Thus his doctor saw him, in Dickensian mood. And thus Churchill was carried by two MPs into Parliament for his last appearance, sixty years after his first; it was Question Time, he sat silent, wondering if the House was talking about him.

In the summer of 1962, Churchill fractured his femur in Monte Carlo and was flown home by the RAF to cheering crowds. His carotid arteries were lined with clots which crumbled into the circulation, causing blocking of blood in the brain; in January 1965 he predictably suffered a third stroke, lingered a fortnight, and was announced dead by his doctor outside his front door in Hyde Park Gate.

This privileged frequenter of official bedrooms had cast a medical eye of intelligent observation on the stars of the wartime scene relaxing or wrangling behind impenetrable doors. Lord Moran published an 800-page book on his intimate relationship with his patient, before the thunder of Churchill's funeral drums had rolled away from the nation's ears. It occasioned severe tut-tutting from important members of the medical profession, who had not themselves the material to make several million quid from such an assured best seller.

> The profession of medicine and surgery must always rank as the most noble that man can adopt. The spectacle of a doctor in action among soldiers (or sailors) in equal danger and with equal courage, saving life where all others are taking it, allaying pain where all others are causing it, is one which must always seem glorious, whether to God or man.

Churchill was not wholly disdainful of doctors, after all.

$\mathcal{S}$TALIN

1879–1953

IN THE AUTUMN of 1952, Stalin returned to Moscow from his holiday at Sochi, on the eastern shores of the Black Sea, not feeling much better. He still had attacks of dizziness, and the energy which had propelled him from being a theology student in Georgia to being the world's current terror was leaking away. His pile of official papers, his extracts and translations of newspapers, he fingered listlessly and tossed aside, shortly sparing himself such daily irritation by directing his secretariat to send no more. He was pale, looked his age, and no longer flew—he had not flown to the wartime summit at Teheran ten years earlier. He was suffering severely from hypertension.

'The great Stalin, the wise leader and teacher, the organiser and inspirer of the historic victories of the Soviet people, the genius of all progressive mankind,' (according to *Pravda*) wore every day a simple grey-brown uniform, buttoned round the neck and tucked into high boots, with (like Hitler) a single medal. He dined plainly, usually off pork, at one o'clock in the morning, retired at four a.m. and rose at noon. He kept a mustard-coloured outfit, with broad red stripes running down the trousers and the shoulders loaded with gold braid, for appearances on the international stage. These polemics were well nourished with caviar, smoked salmon and sucking-pig, and drenched in vodka. The vegetarian politician Sir Stafford Cripps (of whom Churchill inquired, eyeing his dinner plate: 'Are you about to eat that or have you finished?') was unhappy whether caviar was fish, or eggs, which he could not ingest. Stalin confessed ignorance and indifference. He relished playing the modest emperor.

On 6 November, Stalin arrived amid his team of a dozen bodyguards at the Bolshoi to see *Swan Lake*. Generally he invited Molotov to the Bolshoi, and others of his nine-man Bureau hand-picked from the Presidium. The Bureau was usually condensed to four—Comrades Malenkov, Beria, Bulganin and Khrushchev—all summoned at Stalin's caprice. He was growing bored with meetings, particularly when he had decided everything himself first.

But Molotov had fallen out of favour, though he sneaked into the Kremlin cinema when Stalin was going to the movies. Stalin ordered angrily that Molotov be kept in ignorance of his whereabouts; but Khrushchev leaked them, with the idea of softening Stalin's attitude to Molotov by their figuratively sharing the same bag of popcorn. 'Stop this! Stop telling him where I am. I won't tolerate it,' Stalin stormed at Khrushchev when he found out. Thus the highest politics of the USSR progressed.

That night at the ballet, Stalin sat alone in the corner of the second row in his box. The audience repeatedly stood and cheered him loudly. The newly arrived Indian ambassador dutifully assessed him through his opera-glasses, and thought he exuded avuncular benevolence. Before the end of the performance Stalin rose suddenly and left. Perhaps he felt ill, or perhaps it was Comrade Pervukhin, who was desecrating Tchaikovsky in the interval with a long political lecture. Next day, Stalin was standing for hours taking the salute in chilly Red Square at the annual trundling past of the Soviet's nasty weapons.

Stalin's personal physician was Professor Vladimir N. Vinogradov, aged seventy-one, a medical academician, holder of four Orders of Lenin and the Order of the Red Banner of Labour, signatory of the death certificate of President Kalinin six years earlier, acknowledged in Russian medicine as was Churchill's physician Lord Moran in Harley Street. Professor Vinogradov examined Stalin later that month, decided that his condition had deteriorated and advised him to stop serious work forthwith. Stalin was outraged and fired him.

Shortly after the consultation, Stalin received a letter from Dr Lydia Timashuk, an electrocardiograph specialist at the Kremlin Polyclinic. She was unknown to him, and equally so in less esoteric medical circles. She warned Stalin that Professor Vinogradov and eight of his similarly distinguished colleagues, whom she helpfully listed, were conspiring 'to cut short the lives of active public figures of the Soviet Union through sabotage medical treatment'.

Stalin immediately ordered the arrest of all nine doctors. He directed how they should be investigated and interrogated: Professor Vinogradov was to be put in chains and the others beaten up. He warned Comrade Ignatiev, head of the KGB: 'If you do not obtain confessions from the doctors we will shorten you by a head.' Ignatiev was a nice fellow, considerate, mild-mannered, popular with his colleagues, himself suffering from cardiac disease, according to Khrushchev, who described the two comrades' further phone calls: 'Stalin was crazy with rage, yelling at Ignatiev and threatening him, demanding that he throw the doctors into chains, beat them to pulp and grind them into powder.'

A difficult patient.

'Apart from his other unfavourable qualities,' Comrade Beria told Stalin mildly, 'the professor has a very long tongue. He has told one of the doctors in his clinic that Comrade Stalin has already had several dangerous hypertonic episodes.'

'Right,' said Stalin. 'Have the doctors confessed?'

Beria assured him confidently that they shortly would. 'We'll complete the investigation and come for your permission to arrange a public trial.'

'Arrange it,' said Stalin.

Under the treatment, all the doctors confessed to crimes which they had first heard about upon their arrest. While assisting the KGB with their inquiries, two of them died. Beria *en passant* uncovered a subtle murder, of Comrade Zhdanov, by falsifying his electrocardiograph and letting him work on after his coronary thrombosis, until he dropped dead. Professor Vinogradov meanwhile startlingly revealed himself a veteran employee of British Intelligence, for which, at least, Stalin entertained the warmest respect.

Stalin thrust the bundle of doctors' confessions at Khrushchev, snorting that his ministers were as blind as newborn kittens. 'What will happen without me?' he speculated testily. 'The country will perish because you do not know how to recognise enemies.'

The country which Stalin had saved from its internal foes with such commendable briskness knew nothing of its peril until 15 January 1953, when *Pravda* ran the story of the 'Doctors' Plot'. Dr Timashuk herself was a grandmother, her only son killed in the air force. On 20 January, she was invested by the Presidium of the Supreme Soviet with the Order of Lenin, for services in the unmasking of murderous doctors. She was floodlit by *Pravda* and *Izvestia* as a national heroine, commanding thanks for 'restoring the honour and purity of the white gown'. The vile murderers in professorial disguise had been systematically ruining the health of the Soviet top brass, whose mass demotion to the sick list clearly imperilled the national defences. *Pravda* listed three marshals, a general and an admiral who had escaped the fatal treatment, and two members of the Politburo who unfortunately had not. Dr Timashuk had squashed the filthy vermin of secret enemies from creeping capitalism, who had appeared on the floorboards through the deplorable incompetence of the Soviet intelligence services, said *Pravda*, and everyone was now advised keenly to watch out.

The deadly carnival was staged by Comrade Ryumin, deputy head of the KGB. Khrushchev revealed afterwards that Dr Timashuk was a KGB informer, ordered to write the letter to Stalin by Ryumin, who had been ordered to fix some spectacular trials by Stalin, who later had him shot.

On 17 February, the new Indian ambassador called on Stalin in the Kremlin, and dutifully observed his doodling. Stalin was griping that the Americans were determined to widen the Korean war for more business and bigger profits: 'It is no use preaching morals at them, because they are out to accumulate profits even at the price of blood.' The ambassador was stealthily eying Stalin's red pencil drawing wolves—single wolves, pairs of snarling wolves, a wolf on its hind legs, a pack of wolves all over the paper. 'The Russian peasant is a very simple man,' Stalin explained grimly, 'but a very wise one. When the wolf attacks him, he does not attempt to teach it morals but tries to kill it.' He grinned chillingly. 'I am the simple, wise peasant.'

The doctors' plot looked more explosive through six of the doctors being Jews. For centuries, anti-Semitism had been a way of Russian life, but defeat of Hitler left the feeling that they could hardly go on imitating his policies. The organisation of suspected assassins was the American Jewish Joint Distribution Committee, which one doctor confessed had ordered him 'to wipe out the leading cadres of the USSR'. To make his point, Stalin arrested several medical, academic and administrative Jews and a Jewish bandleader; shot a Jewish general who had wisely fled to the banks of the Volga; and broke off diplomatic relations with Israel.

His idea was to transport Russian Jews to northern Siberia, where they would die unobtrusively from starvation and hypothermia. Molotov's wife Zemchuzhina, who had run the beauty industry in the USSR, was already there, but it did not seem to bother Molotov.

It was cold and blustery in Moscow that late February, but a more bitter chill caught the Soviet rulers. They shivered at the prospect of another widespread purge and programme of show trials. They readily remembered the senior Russian officers who had prospected an alliance with Germany: when the plan leaked through Prague, Stalin shot four thousand officers above the rank of Colonel *pour encourager les autres*.

On the last day of the month, Stalin was feeling better. He rose late in his dacha, read the reports from Korea, enjoyed a short walk and held a meeting with Beria and Khrushchev and his other intimates. He decided to instruct the North Koreans to get the best deal they could and stop fighting. He sat up until four in the morning, the others growing tired, he growing irritated, using the doctors' plot as a text to sermonise his uneasy visitors that past glories never keep you in top jobs. He stopped in mid-sentence, rose and went to bed. The comrades went home in silence.

At 6.30 the next evening, Stalin had not appeared nor rang. No one dared enter his room unbidden. He had suffered a cerebral haemorrhage. This was tackled by the reserve team of doctors. He was the last grandee in Europe to be treated with leeches, but they did not do him any good.

Before closing down in the early hours of 4 March, Moscow

Radio announced that Stalin had been elected to the Moscow City Soviet. At six, it resumed with Beethoven and women's choirs instead of light music. It went off the air. The listeners were unconcerned. It had broken down before. The presses at *Pravda* had meanwhile been halted. At eight, the radio announced Stalin's illness. He died next day. Nobody bothered about the doctors' plot any more.

'We knew some of these people personally because they had once treated us,' Khrushchev remarked chivalrously afterwards. 'When we examined this case after Stalin's death, we found it to be fabricated from beginning to end.'

'A single death is an incident of consequence and pathos, but the death of a million is a matter of statistics,' Stalin had observed, ever the modest mass murderer.

FRANKLIN D. ROOSEVELT

1882–1945

FROM 1941 TO 1945—between Lend-Lease end Yalta—the United States National Naval Medical Center at Bethesda in Maryland admitted Mr James D. Elliot, Mr Delano, Mr F. D. Rolphe and twenty-six other gentlemen of various names for treatment. All of them were recognisable instantly as the President of the United States. However secretive their entries and exits, the news must have buzzed excitedly round the personnel. Wartime security prevented its leaking outside so effectively that a search today produces no records of these patients in the US Navy files, nor any note of a Mr Roosevelt being among them. What investigations and treatment the President invoked, how long he stayed, or why he was there at all, are ghosts beyond recall of the Freedom of Information Act.

In August 1921, Roosevelt took a yachting trip to the family summer resort, tiny Campobello Island off New Brunswick, opposite Nova Scotia across the icy Bay of Fundy, in which he commendably had a swim. He was thirty-nine, and had savoured politics as Woodrow Wilson's assistant-secretary of the Navy. That night he shivered, and complained that he had caught cold. He had been worryingly ill only once before, with typhoid in 1912, when 'Typhoid Mary' and her carefree fellow-carriers were richly infecting the New York State of which he had just become a senator.

In the morning at Campobello, Roosevelt's right knee was weak, by afternoon he was unable to stand on his right leg, that evening the left knee went, the next morning he could not stand at all. His temperature was 102°F. Next day, he found himself paralysed from the chest down—also in the balls of his thumbs, irritatingly stopping him writing.

The local doctor was alarmed, and summoned a retired neuro-surgeon on vacation, who diagnosed spinal thrombosis. They called in Dr Lovett, a specialist physician from Boston, who diagnosed poliomyelitis. This has become a rare viral disease since Jonas Salk in 1954 discovered the immunising vaccine, which can be swallowed in the first year of life. In 1921, polio was a terror of childhood, and a hazard for adults who had acquired no immunity, particularly those reared in the more hygienic wealthier areas of the United States.

For a fortnight, Roosevelt endured catheterisation and bowel incontinence. After three weeks, he was moved to a New York hospital, and in November back home to 65th Street. Dr Lovett, who fizzed with the optimism of Roosevelt's later medical attendants, spoke of recuperation: but muscles which do not recover in a month never will. Roosevelt ended with paralysed legs and a waist weak on the right. In February 1922, braces were fitted from his hips to his feet, first in steel weighing seven pounds, and two years later in aluminum weighing half as much. He experimented dragging himself back to his job at 120 Broadway, where he was branch head of an insurance company on $25,000 a year.

The Roosevelts—once the van Roosevelts from Holland—were untitled aristocrats surveying their New York estates as naturally as the earls of England their counties. Franklin D. Roosevelt went to Groton school, Harvard, then the Columbia Law School, though without getting a degree (it was interfering with his social life). He managed the New York State Bar examination, so could practise law, and became an unremarkable clerk for various Wall Street lawyers. He told them that he was certainly not doing law forever, but reckoned he had a good chance of being President.

A half-paralysed patient makes a difficult politician. Will the voters spurn him as a broken-down vehicle for their burning convictions? Or take to him as an obvious sufferer of the miseries they all endure? This attitude could be particularly useful in the Great Depression. No opposition would cruelly indict him as 'a cripple'—that could be counterproductive. Perhaps the electorate does not care, politicians being unreal effigies paraded periodically through everyday life.

Like our Nelson without arm or eye, Roosevelt cruised under billowing sails to his Trafalgar. In 1929 he became Governor of New York, and in 1932 was awarded the presidency, presenting the country in return with a catchy New Deal ('I obtained my "New Deal" slogan from Mark Twain's *A Connecticut Yankee*,' he confessed in 1933), and more immediately appreciable, the repeal of prohibition.

The Republicans uncharitably suggested that a wheelchair and regularly taking the waters at Warm Springs, Georgia, were dubious luxuries for the White House. The Democrats retaliated with a resounding medical examination of a fifty-year-old man splendidly mobile on crutches. The report mentioned also a blood pressure of 140/100 (normal, 120/80) and an electrocardiogram depicting left-sided cardiac enlargement and lessened coronary blood-flow—the unnoticed viper in the herb-garden where everything was lovely.

When Roosevelt became President, Vice-Admiral Ross T. McIntire became his doctor. He attended him each morning and night, with the regal sycophancy of Sir James Reid, physician to Queen Victoria. 'The President,' McIntire was informed reassuringly by the Admiral appointing him, 'is strong as a horse with the exception of a chronic sinus condition that makes him susceptible to colds. That's where you come in.'

McIntire was an ear, nose and throat man, who did miracles for Roosevelt's chronic sinusitis. He had a hearty sea-dog bedside manner: he advised his paralysed patient 'to lick it', and if becoming tired to 'quit the grind', and he publicly dismissed undue loss of weight with praise of his new 'flat—repeat, f-l-a-t tummy'. Roosevelt thought he was wonderful. Whatever difficulties Roosevelt presented, he was always charming to his doctors.

Doctors who specialise in one portion of the body somewhat regard the rest of it as existing only to supply their bit's vital needs. McIntire appointed his subordinate, Commander Howard Bruenn, as officer in command of the presidential heart. Roosevelt's succeeding presidential terms, running into the war, were thus of medical confusion.

His blood pressure continued rising, his heart enlarging and his coronary flow decreasing, in an era when there was nothing the doctors could do to stop it. It was the natural course of the disease. He began to look ill. It was hardly necessary for the Republicans to allege that he had suffered a 'coronary thrombosis, a brain haemorrhage, a nervous breakdown, an aneurysm of the aorta, and a cancerous prostate,' also an operation at the Mayo Clinic for carcinoma of the rectum. Roosevelt *was* operated on, in January 1944, but only for the removal of a wen from the back of his head.

That spring of 1944, he had been coughing for two months, and friends were joining opponents in counter-advising a fourth term. Press conferences were being cancelled, and the press was bubbling with gloom. The medical cabal kept the progressive severity of the President's failing circulation from the world so efficiently that the patient's outside doctors, the patient—indeed, the intimate doctors themselves—seemed hardly aware of it. 'The President's health is perfectly OK. There are absolutely no organic difficulties at all,' Vice-Admiral McIntire was comforting the nation and its allies.

On 10 May 1944, Roosevelt was examined by five doctors (probably under a pseudonym at the Bethesda Medical Center). Since 1931, the Democrats had been defending him with medical reports inclined to optimism, if not euphoria. The doctors, including a professor from George Washington University, now reported: 'As before, apical impulse is in the anterior axillary line'. This peak of the heartbeat should have been within the line of the middle of the clavicle. The heart was greatly enlarged. Bafflingly, this did not alarm them. They recorded no blood-pressure examination, no electrocardiograph findings, and no suggestion of treatment. Had they performed similarly in their qualifying examination, all five would have been ploughed on the spot.

To make sure, McIntire persuaded the President to have another examination a fortnight later, when a doctor from Atlanta preached a medical parable about an automobile's engine and tyres wearing out after 40,000 miles at seventy miles an hour. McIntire admitted 'a moderate degree of arteriosclerosis', a vague term for arterial degeneration with age; but the only arteries they could see, through an ophthalmoscope in the retina, were normal. He agreed also, 'some changes in the cardiographic tracing'. He recommended his patient have rest and sunshine. He had a liking for the comfortably curative—though, poor man, he had nothing more curative to prescribe. After some argument, Bruenn won permission to administer digitalis, the traditional heart remedy discovered in the Shropshire villagers' foxglove tea in 1775, which slows the pulse and strengthens the beat. If Roosevelt needed digitalis, he was slipping towards heart failure.

In August 1944, Roosevelt made an ineffective speech in a gale at the Bremerton naval yard opposite Seattle at Puget Sound, and had an attack of angina. To his two doctors' relief, an immediate electrocardiogram showed 'no unusual pathology'. This attack of angina was recorded as his only one, which is unlikely. In the desperate minutes before Roosevelt's death, Bruenn telephoned McIntire that he was 'continuing to use aminophylline, nitroglycerin, and other remedies'. Aminophylline was then used for heart failure, and nitroglycerin relieves the agonising spasm of angina. But whatever drugs the President was taking regularly in the last year of his life remain secret remedies.

In April, the President spent a month at Bernard Baruch's South Carolina plantation, while McIntire fussed over his diet to prevent some irritating farting. There he had two attacks of gallstone colic, which a later x-ray in Washington confirmed by revealing the gallstones, and which McIntire overlooked in his report. 'He was out on the water every day, handling a rod and tackle with all his old strength,' the Admiral proclaimed proudly when they returned to the White House, though admitting that the President had piles.

Another examination on November 1 showed a blood pressure which rose to 180/100 from 'small annoyances'. The President could lie flat without difficulty in breathing, he had no fluid bubbling at the base of his lungs, so he had no signs of heart failure. The doctors found him 'in good condition for a man of his age', though tired, and recommended ultraviolet light and vitamins. 'The heart deserved to be watched,' McIntire conceded. He recommended a rest after lunch and early bed, but the war intruded.

In January 1945, the President went to Yalta. He sailed in the USS *Quincy* to Malta, then flew to the Crimea with an escort of six fighters, at 6,000 feet. Churchill flew with an oxygen mask. Stalin never flew at all. Churchill's doctor Lord Moran encountered Roosevelt on the snow-swept Crimean airfield:

> The President looked old and thin and drawn; he had a cape or shawl over his shoulders and appeared shrunken; he sat looking straight ahead with his mouth open, as if he were not taking things in. Everyone was shocked by his appearance and gabbled about it afterwards.

It was on the field of the Charge of the Light Brigade that Moran reflected:

> To a doctor's eye, the President appears a very sick man. He has all the symptoms of hardening of the arteries of the brain in an advanced stage, so that I give him only a few months to live. But men shut their eyes when they do not want to see, and the Americans here cannot bring themselves to believe that he is finished. His daughter thinks that he is not really ill, and his doctor backs her up.

Before leaving England at the end of January, Moran had a sweepingly contradictory letter from a former President of the American College of Physicians:

> Roosevelt had heart failure eight months ago. There are, of course, degrees of congestive failure, but Roosevelt had enlargement of his liver and was puffy. A post-mortem would have shown congestion of his organs. He was irascible and became very irritable if he had to concentrate his mind for long. If anything was brought up that wanted thinking out he would change the subject. He was, too, sleeping badly.

All this seems to have escaped the notice of his personal physician. McIntire complained, hurt, in 1946: 'I am adjudged as having deliberately deceived the people of the United States by the issuance of statements that the President was sound organically and in fairly good health.'

In the next fifty years, he was joined in the smoke-screen by the physicians of Presidents Pompidou and Mitterand.

Postwar Europe was arranged at Yalta by three men aged seventy, sixty-five, and sixty-three, by brains which would submit to fatal massive strokes from their arteries, respectively twenty years, eight years, and two months ahead.

On 12 April 1945, Roosevelt was passing a month at Warm Springs. 'After a hearty breakfast that he enjoyed, the patient seemed in high spirits,' McIntire in Washington cheerily recalled Commander Bruenn's morning report. 'The end, therefore, came with shocking suddenness.'

Roosevelt was waiting for lunch at 1.20, chatting to his secretary and three women and making a joke. He suddenly complained of a headache, slumped unconscious and at 3.35 was dead.

Commander Bruenn had rushed wet from the pool. Ever the optimist, he reported to McIntire in Washington that the unconscious President's pulse was excellent and his blood pressure falling. An intracardiac injection of adrenalin was given, so often the medical last rite. Cause of death was a 'massive intercerebral hemorrhage which, in all probability, had ruptured into the subarachnoid space.'

Roosevelt had lately been complaining of 'drawing a blank', moments of loss of speech. These were 'TIAs', temporary ischaemic attacks, which in the 1940s were unidentified. A speck of clot from the chambers of the heart, or from the carotid arteries, lodges in a small artery and knocks out a bit of the brain. Another massive clot, rather than a haemorrhage, could have caused his death.

A post-mortem was considered unnecessary.

The news reached Berlin during an air-raid that night. Goebbels returned from making a speech to the officers of Ninth Army headquarters on the Eastern front, to encounter his aide Rudolf Semmler.

Semmler, together with other members of Goebbels' staff, met him on the steps of the Ministry and told him the glad news the moment he got out of his car. Semmler noticed Goebbels turn pale; the news must have seemed quite incredible. He ordered champagne to be served in his study. He rang Hitler at once at the Chancellery, speaking in a tense, excited voice, words that were later remembered by some of those present.

'My Führer,' he said, 'I congratulate you. Roosevelt is dead. Fate has laid low your greatest enemy. God has not abandoned us. A miracle has happened. This is like the death of the Empress Elizabeth in the Seven Years' War. It is written in the stars that the second half of April will be the turning point for us. This is Friday 13th April. It is the turning point.'

After fighting it for five and a half years, the Nazis had no conception of democracy. Soon Truman and then Attlee were in place. The great men had gone, but it was not the end of the world—except for Goebbels and Hitler. Roosevelt was a middle-aged man with a rising blood pressure that finally burst or choked an artery. It was a necessary end.

Admiral McIntire wrote of 1944:

The problem now was to protect the President's reserve strength, with constant watch on the heart, and this became the particular business of Commander Howard Bruenn. Let me say, parenthetically, that the supervisory care of this young doctor would have added years to the patient's life but for the sudden and unforeseen cerebral hemorrhage. Proof is furnished by the fact that the President's heart functioned strongly to the very last.

Or, as the surgeons say: 'The operation was successful, but the patient died.'

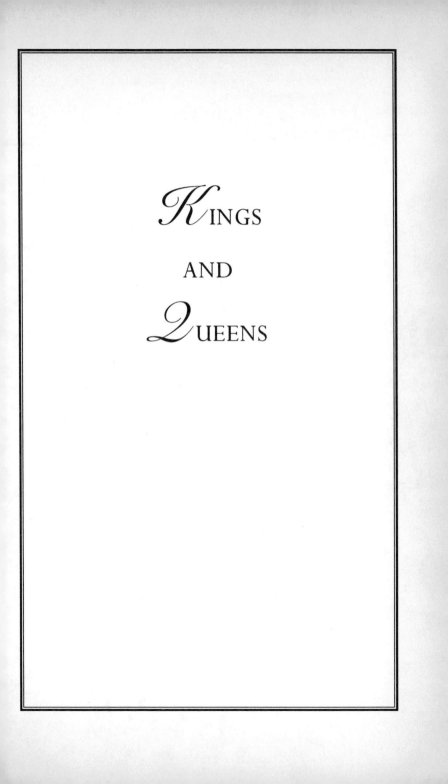

KINGS AND QUEENS

CHARLES II

1630–1685

CHARLES II WAS A difficult patient. He was an unconscionable time dying.

Precisely at eight o'clock His Most Serene Majesty King Charles the Second, having just left his bed, was walking about quietly in his bed-chamber, when he felt some unusual disturbance in his brain, which was soon followed by loss of speech and convulsions of some violence.

There happened to be present at the time two in all of the King's Physicians, and they, so as promptly to forestal so serious a danger to the best of Kings, opened a vein in his right arm, and drew off about sixteen ounces of blood. Meantime too the rest of the Physicians had been summoned by express messengers, and flocked quickly to the King's assistance; and after they had held a consultation together, they strenuously endeavoured to afford timely succour to His Majesty in his dangerous state.

Whitehall was a straggling, jumbled Palace beside the Thames with room for 2,000 courtiers, where Charles had lived since arriving in London from Dover after the Restoration of 1660. That morning, he rose in the apartments of one of his mistresses, the Duchess of Portsmouth. The emergency was enlarged upon in his diary by John Evelyn, a favourite of the King's since their meeting in Paris in 1646, when Charles was in exile and the diarist was wisely reining his royalist enthusiasm from participating at home in the Civil War.

> If by God's providence, Dr King (that excellent chirurgeon as well as physician) had not been accidentally present to let him blood with his lances in his pocket, his Majesty had certainly died that moment, which might have been of direful consequence, there being nobody else with the King save his doctor and one more, as I am assured: it was a mark of the extraordinary dexterity, resolution, and presentness of judgment to let him blood in the very paroxysm, without staying the coming of other physicians, which regularly should have been done, and for not doing so, must have a formal pardon as they tell me.

The messengers who spurred from the royal cobblestones gathered a team of physicians which rose, over the coming week, to the strength of an England rugger side. To have two doctors is dangerous; to have fifteen is fatal.

They were the fashionable doctors of London, who gave consultations in the coffee-houses at half a guinea a time, and they cost the King a hundred guineas a year each. Well-breeched, gold-braided, full-wigged, tricorn-hatted, silk-stockinged, they had silver buckles on their feet and in their fingers the gold-headed cane. This was the physician's professional symbol, his healing wand, the equivalent of today's slung stethoscope. The golden head was perforated, creating an inhaler of fragrant herbs, or of pungent Marseilles vinegar, optimistically believed to overcome the infection of the sickroom, or at least its stink.

The congregating royal doctors immediately bettered their quick-witted herald by removing another eight ounces of blood through cupping-glasses and scarification. Captain of the Medical XV was Sir Charles Scarburgh, who left an enlightening case report in Latin:

> Within a few moments after this, so as to free his stomach of all impurities, and by the same action to rid his whole nervous system of anything harmful to it, they administered an Emetic,

to wit, half an ounce of Orange Infusion of the metals, made in white wine. And as only a small part of this was taken, so that their endeavour might not be altogether frustrated, they added one drachm of white vitriol, this to drain away the humours more speedily by his nether channels. Further, so as to accelerate the operation of that Purgative, they supplemented it with an Enema.

As ours is the age of the fashionable diet, King Charles's golden days were those of the clyster. This hefty brass enema syringe, with a three-inch nozzle like a fire-hose, enjoyed the therapeutic attraction of producing swift and obvious results. It was more reliable than an emetic, the alternative ejective treatment.

Half a century after William Harvey had announced the circulation of the blood, the principle of seventeenth-century medicine remained thus: doctors having not the faintest idea of what caused disease, the best course was vigorously to expel from the body whatever it was.

Spectacular emission through man's normal entrance and exit could be supplemented by the nose, the sweat glands and the hair follicles. Letting out the diseased blood directly seemed a sound idea, though it had notably failed to work for the Black Death, and suffered lunar complications:

> Three special months, September, April, May
> There are in which 'tis good to ope a vein.
> In these three months the moon bears greatest sway.

Such admirably forthright medical philosophy rendered treatment, though useless, noticeably uncomfortable.

The King had a fragrant enema:

The ingredients were mallow leaves, violets, pellitory, beet, herb mercurial, camomile flowers, fennel seeds, linseed, plain waters, cinnamon, zedoaria, avarum, cardamom seeds, saffron, cochineal, and aloes.

Unfortunately, it did not work:

After one or two hours they repeated the Clyster, with the addition of 2 ounces of Syrup of Buckthorn, 4 ounces of Antimonal Wine, and 2 drachms of Rock Salt. Over and above this, so as to leave no stone unturned, Blistering Agents were applied all over his head, after his hair had been shaved.

Then horror! The red-hot cautery was requisitioned. But to the doctors' elation full consciousness returned, and its application was mercifully judged superfluous.

The King recounted his rising from bed to be shaved, feeling unwell and reaching into his closet for the 'King's Drops', a volatile extract of bone made in his own lab ('he had a laboratory and knew of many empirical medicines, and the easier mechanical mathematics,' John Evelyn noted). The drops had been commended by the royal doctors' contemporary Dr Sydenham, memorable as 'the English Hippocrates'. Such a pity they had not invited him to join the team.

The physicians pronounced the King out of immediate danger, but met in consultation knowing they had work to do. Sir Charles related:

As evening came on, so as to persevere in their object of diverting and withdrawing the humours from his head, and at the same time to give strength to his loaded brain, they prescribed Sacred Bitter Powder and Bryony Compound, to be taken as often and in such quantities, as the Physicians present may deem advisable. Bryony is reputed to be emetic, purgative, and diuretic. At the same time, so as to excite sneezing, a powder was prepared of a drachm of White Hellebore roots, to be kept in readiness to be applied to the King's nostrils, as occasion arose. A second Powder also was made up out of 4 ounces of Cowslip flowers (to strengthen his brain). So as to keep his bowels active at night as well, the following remedy was prescribed: Cream of Tartar in Barley Water, two-hourly. At the same time, so as to counteract the scalding of his urine, likely to result from the use of blistering drugs, an Emulsion was made up of Liquorice and Sweet Almond Kernels.

Between doses, the patient supped on thin broth and a draught of light ale made without hops.

Spirit of Sal Ammoniac was applied now and again to His Most Serene Majesty's nostrils, both as a cerebral stimulant, and to excite sneezing. So as to leave nothing at all untried, to promote still further both the revulsion and the derivation from his Head, Cephalic Plasters combined with Spurge and Burgundy Pitch, in equal parts, were applied to the soles of his feet. The ingredient of this plaster was pigeon's dung.

So ended the first day's treatment. The poor doctors must have been exhausted.

The gorgeous gatherings from the English countryside were given again the next morning, unworthily to produce their nauseous or colicky effects. 'The Physicians ordered His Most Serene Majesty to go on taking the Sacred Tincture,' Sir Charles reported comfortably. The King had difficulty in peeing—the foreseen scalding urine, from the 'Spanish Fly' cantharides in his head plasters—so at noon they opened both his jugulars and drew off ten ounces of blood.

The bowels were conscientiously kept active by Best Manna in Chicken Broth, and a gargle of Inner bark of Elm in Barley Water was presented for his sore throat, occasioned by the doctors' trying to prize open his teeth during his fits. To cheer him up, they prescribed a Julep of Black Cherry Water, Flowers of Lime, Lilies of the valley, Paeony Compound, Spirit of Lavender, Prepared Pearls and White Sugar Candy, 'of which he might sip, as often as he pleased,' which sounds delightful, and even better with a slug of gin.

Next morning, the Privy Council announced in the *London Gazette* that His Majesty had been seized with a violent fit, that gave great cause to fear the issue of it, but by the application of proper and reasonable remedies the physicians conceived 'that he will in a few days be freed from his distemper'.

That night, the King became so ill that they added to his Julep forty drops of Spirit of Human Skull—its donor the recipient of a violent death gloomily perceived by Sir Charles Scarburgh as 'a sure harbinger of impending dissolution'. By the morning he had improved, providing his physicians with the brilliant notion of his having suffered all the time from intermittent fever. There was a lot of it about in London that winter.

This was an invaluable diagnosis, because Lord North, the Lord Chancellor, and the King's ministers were asking with increasing irritation what exactly was *wrong with him*? The doctors could but learnedly shake their heads, and mutter about the humours of his brain. Now they even had a cure. Chinchona bark, yielding quinine, had been popularised by Dr Sydenham for stopping the ague. It was a specific remedy, the isolated forerunner of William Withering's foxglove for dropsy in 1775 and Florey's penicillin of 1940.

Cinchona bark had been discovered about 1630 by the Countess of Chinchon, her husband being the Spanish Viceroy in Peru, and exported to Europe by the Jesuits to allay the strangely intermittent fever of malaria. (That the Countess of Chinchon died before reaching Peru, that nobody had any conception of mosquitoes spreading malaria, that much of the bark reaching avid Europe from Peru was profitably adulterated, are unnecessary complications to a success story.) Fragments of 'Jesuits' bark' swirled in the religious tempests which swept bloodily to and fro across Britain over these centuries: Oliver Cromwell choked on the stuff. The King took his chinchona bark three times a day, between his Spirit of Human Skull.

On Thursday, 5 February, the religious winds breezed into the royal sickroom. Charles was a Protestant king, but suspected of having a Catholic soul. His brother James, who was gloomily fussing about with the physicians, was intent on Catholicising the country upon his imminent succession. About eight o'clock that night, John Hudleston, the Benedictine monk who had saved Charles's life when he escaped with £1,000 on his head after the Battle of Worcester, was summoned secretly to Whitehall with his ecclesiastical kit for the dying. 'The King then declared himself that he desired to die in the faith and communion of the Holy Roman Catholic Church': and Father Hudleston obliged him. 'I hope it is not true; but these busy emissaries are very forward upon such occasions,' commented John Evelyn when he heard about it.

That Thursday, the King had suffered another attack of convulsions. But his mind remained clear enough to request his brother not to let poor Nelly starve.

As the illness was now becoming more grave and His Most Serene Majesty's strength (Woe's me!) gradually failing the Physicians were compelled to have recourse to the more active Cardiac Tonics, and to prescribe the following: Raleigh's Stronger Antidote, ½ drachm. (The Confectio Raleighana was an extract of different parts of an enormous number of herbs, animals, etc.)

The case was desperate. They gave him the Goa Stone. Then the oriental Bezoar Stone, from the stomach of an East Indian goat (they needed to beware of imitations).

But (alas!) after an ill-fated night His Serene Majesty's strength seemed exhausted to such a degree, that the whole assemblage of Physicians lost all hope and became despondent.

Thus Sir Charles threw in the well-stained towel. The team met for 'this last and most dismal meeting,' the patient grew breathless and speechless, 'and he peacefully laid down his mortal Crown to take up the Immortal' shortly after noon on Friday, 6 February.

As anyone of importance who died was flattered with the suspicion of being poisoned, they held a post-mortem. They found:

On the Surface of the Brain the Veins and Arteries were unduly full. All the Cerebral ventricles were filled with a kind of serous matter, and the substance of the brain itself was quite soaked with similar fluid.

49

They found, also, the remains of a right-sided pleurisy. The King probably died from cerebral thrombosis, or from cerebral emboli—causing his two attacks of fits—by clots loosed from the lining of his arteries or his heart. Two centuries after his deathbed, Matthew Arnold could still shudder:

> *Nor bring, to see me cease to live,*
> *Some doctor full of phrase and fame,*
> *To shake his sapient head and give*
> *The ill he cannot cure a name.*

John Evelyn remembered fondly of Charles:

He took delight to have a number of little spaniels follow him, and lie in his bed-chamber, where often times he suffered the bitches to puppy and give suck, which rendered it very offensive, and indeed made the whole Court nasty and stinking: an excellent prince doubtless had he been less addicted to women, which made him uneasy and always in want to supply their unmeasurable profusion.

On 1 February 1685:

I am never to forget the unexpressible luxury, and profaneness, gaming, and all dissolution, and as it were total forgetfulness of God (it being Sunday evening) which this day sennight, I was witness of; the King, sitting and toying with his concubines, Portsmouth, Cleveland, and Mazarine, etc: a French boy singing love songs, in that glorious Gallery, whilst about 20 of the great courtiers and other dissolute persons were at Basset round a large table, a bank of at least 2000 in gold before them, upon which two gentlemen that were with me made reflexions with astonishment, it being a scene of utmost vanity; and surely as they thought would never have an end: six days after was all in the dust.

Charles died more lingeringly but less agonisingly than his father, who departed English history with a cut severing his fourth cervical vertebra.

$\mathcal{A}$NNE

1665–1714

QUEEN ANNE IS DEAD, and so are her eighteen children, who drew barely a breath of air between them.

Anne was the daughter of James II, the brother of the unconscionably long-dying Charles II. She was the younger sister of Mary, who in 1677 married William of Orange and jointly succeeded to the throne when her father James was kicked off it in 1688.

Anne's mother—Anne Hyde, of a mere county family—died when Anne was six, her death revealing that both parents had secretly turned Roman Catholic. Then James at forty remarried (by proxy) fifteen-year-old Mary Modena, an Italian Princess, a Catholic seduced from the very doors of a convent. In June 1688, this Mary gave birth to another James, who became the 'Old Pretender' of the 1715 Jacobite rebellion, though he was widely believed to be some little stranger smuggled into her bed at St James's Palace in a warming-pan. The attending doctor got a knighthood and the midwife five hundred guineas 'for your breakfast'.

Panicking over Protestant heirs, Parliament placed Anne under the tutorship of the Bishop of London, who built her into a Protestant bastion like Wren's shining new St Paul's Cathedral. This liturgical schism—Catholic or Anglican—had ignited the Civil War, and would still bring to British soil the battles of Sedgemoor, the Boyne and Culloden. Nothing like religion for cutting throats.

Teenage brides frisked through the courts of Europe like prize puppies. When Anne was fifteen, her marriage was mooted to George Ludwig, the eighteen-year-old Prince of Hanover, despite his mother's objecting that she came from a very ordinary family. George Ludwig included Anne in his Grand Tour of 1680, but he did not take to her, and stayed out of her country until he returned, not as a tourist, but as George I.

On 28 July 1683, when she was eighteen, Anne married another George, of Denmark. He was thirty, pockmarked, a constructor of model ships, fat and lazy (obviously, not sexually). In the vision of the portrait painters, she was comely and portly with lovely hands. It was a happy marriage, in which George came to love only 'his news, his bottle, and the Queen.' He was an asthmatic, and 'sometimes they wept, sometimes they mourned in words, but hand-in-hand, he sick in his bed, she the carefulest nurse to him that can be imagined'.

On 12 May 1684, Anne had a stillborn daughter. This was ascribed to a fall from a horse, like many medical calamities at the time. She spent summer taking the waters at Tunbridge Wells, and on 2 June 1685 had a daughter, Mary. Like her mother, the child suffered from runny eyes (probably a blocked tear duct), also from impetigo. She died on 8 February 1687, from 'an infection'. She was buried in Westminster Abbey in the vault of the headless Mary Queen of Scots, who herself was first buried in Peterborough Cathedral but sepulchrally upgraded by her son, James I.

On 12 May 1686, two hours after arriving at Windsor Castle, Anne had a premature daughter, Anne Sophia. The baby succumbed to the same infection a week before her sister, and was buried in Westminster Abbey under the lovely fan vaulting of Henry VII's Chapel. Post-mortems were performed: 'the eldest was all consumed, but the youngest very sound and likely to live'. *What* infection is unknown. Perhaps they died from smallpox, from which their mother was immune after an attack at the age of twelve. Smallpox epidemics were then ravaging the families of England, and the previous year the diarist John Evelyn had lost his own two daughters within five months.

Three centuries later, smallpox has been eradicated from the world; the unknown army of microbes which stealthily murdered and massacred us is classified and largely vanquished. Why fight over religion, when 'the strength of our salvation' is medicine?

On 21 January next, Anne suffered a 'miscarriage', a term then embracing any foetus expelled at any time during pregnancy. She ascribed it to performing the Riggadoon, a new French dance with 'a great deal of jumping in it'. On 22 October, she had a stillborn child, declared a month dead in utero. At four in the morning of 16 April 1688, she had a miscarriage in the third month of pregnancy. She afterwards presented a pseudocyesis, over which she kept herself coddled in Bath, but the phantom pregnancy unexcitedly faded away.

On Guy Fawkes Day 1688, William of Orange triumphantly landed at Torbay in Devon. On 24 July 1689, at Hampton Court, Anne triumphantly gave birth to William, Duke of Gloucester. Anne's sister Mary, now the Queen, had no children—abortion and infant mortality ran in the family; their own mother had six other children with an average life under two years. Now there was a Prince ensuring the Protestant succession, and yah boo to the baby in the warming-pan.

William was a weakly child. His hydrocephalus was undisguised even by the brushstrokes of Godfrey Kneller. He did not talk until he was three, nor walk until he was five, and could not mount stairs without help (this got him birched by Prince George). He turned eleven, and died of scarlet fever.

On 14 October 1690, at St James's Palace, Anne had a daughter two months premature, who lived two hours. On 17 April 1692, at Syon House beside the Thames, she had a son George, who lived an hour. She had been delivered by the man-midwife Hugh Chamberlen (at a hundred guineas), of the obstetrical Hugenot family who had handled the miscarriage of Charles I's Queen Henrietta (the midwife had fainted from fright), invented the *tire-tête* forceps and kept them a family secret for 125 years.

On 23 March 1693, in St James's Street, Anne had a stillborn daughter. On 21 January 1694, she had a stillborn child of unknown sex. On 17 February 1696, she miscarried a daughter, and on 16 September a son at six months. On 25 March 1697, she miscarried twins of unrecorded sex. That December she had a miscarriage. On 15 September 1698, at Windsor, she had a stillborn son despite cosseting herself after twenty weeks' pregnancy. Post-mortem showed no defects, but the foetus had been dead ten days, and was buried in St George's Chapel, near the headless body of Charles I.

On 24 January 1700 Anne had a stillborn son, six weeks premature and dead for a month, and on 30 July the Duke of Gloucester died. On 21 February 1702, riding in Richmond Park, William II stumbled on a molehill (thus 'the little gentleman in black velvet' became a Jacobite toast), on 8 March he died from his fall and tuberculosis. Her sister Mary having already died of smallpox, Anne was Queen.

Anne was thirty-seven, with obstetrical relief in sight from the menopause (though at the age of forty-five 'the Menses happened to her as if she had been but 20 years old'), and six years later the father of this melancholy procession of infant funerals joined them.

Over sixteen years Anne had:

> 17 pregnancies, producing
> 18 children, represented by
> 6 miscarriages (1 twins)
> 6 stillbirths
> 5 live births.

Of the 5 live births

> 2 survived under 3 hours
> 2 survived under 2 years
> 1 survived under 12 years
> 3 died from non-obstetrical causes.

Why?

1. *Syphilis*.

    Not typical. No signs of congenital syphilis in the living children. Why should the Prince of Denmark have syphilis?

2. *Rhesus disease*.

    Anne Rhesus negative, George Rhesus positive. Not typical. The first child would be normal, the later ones progressively affected.

    But! Anne's first stillbirth might truly have been inflicted by her fall from a horse. Her following two children survived to die in infancy from infection. Then she had three foetuses possibly dead from Rhesus incompatibility. Next, the Duke of Gloucester broke the Rhesus pattern. This raises the interesting possibility of the royal milkman (Rh-negative) being involved.

He could have been Lord Mulgrave, seventeen years older than Anne, who the year before her marriage was buzzed round the Court as her seducer. 'Only ogling,' he protested, but he had sent her intimate letters, was banished and exiled to Tangiers in a frigate (leaky). He returned as Lord Chamberlain, William III created him Marquis of Normanby and Queen Anne promoted him Duke of Buckingham. He married three times, lastly to an illegitimate daughter of James II, who was thus Anne's half-sister. Perhaps that was the nearest they got, after the ogling.

3. *Diabetes.*

Unlikely. The babies would be large.

4. *Placental insufficiency.*

Brings death in utero and weakly babies, and is usually caused by high maternal blood pressure. Anne's blood pressure is unknown, but she was so obese that the block and tackles installed to shift Henry VIII upstairs at Hampton Court needed renewal.

5. *Disseminated lupus erythematosus.*

Anne had a red and spotted face: 'and therefore t'was expedient to use paint to disguise the discolourings; but this was kept so secret that it was never so much as whispered abroad in her lifetime.' 'Butterfly-rash' is typical of this disease, which causes also arthritis: Anne suffered badly from rheumatism and 'gout', an illness then covering a multitude of symptoms.

In 1975, a lupus anticoagulant in the blood was discovered to cause repeated abortion in young women. Perhaps

Anne's were from this unknown cause; perhaps from incompatibility to George's sperm; perhaps from endocrine imbalance or from a cause still unknown to us. Perhaps we are too pernickety about Anne. In her times, when malnutrition, sepsis and medical ignorance abounded, the commonplace death of infants, before or after birth, provoked no more than downcast eyes and a woeful shrug. In 1699, the mortality rate between one and *fourteen* was twenty per cent. How often was the royal obstetrical progress mimicked in a cottage?

As well as a persistent mother, Anne was an enthusiastic lesbian.

Sarah Jennings, later Duchess of Marlborough, was five years older than Anne, and they were childhood friends. Sarah became a lady of the bedchamber, and they later corresponded in intimate social equality, respectively as 'Mrs Morley' and 'Mrs Freeman'. Sarah dominated Anne's feeble personality. On Anne's accession, Sarah became keeper of the privy purse, later deducting £18,000 for nine years' back pension. The inevitable rupture had then occurred. Sarah's cousin Abigail, Mrs Masham, who was ten years younger and a lowly bedchamber *woman*, had been shifted by Anne into Sarah's Kensington apartments.

> *When as Queen Anne of great renown*
> *Great Britain's scepter sway'd*
> *Besides the Church, she dearly lov'd*
> *A dirty chamber-maid.*
>
> *O! Abigail that was her name,*
> *She stitch'd and starch'd full well,*
> *But how she pierc'd this Royal heart,*
> *No mortal man can tell,*

they chuckled round the coffee-houses. On 26 July 1711, Sarah reminded Anne that:

. . . you valued most your reputation, which I confess surpris'd me very much, that your Majesty should so soon mention that word after having discover'd so great a passion for such a woman, for sure there can be no great reputation in a thing so strange & unaccountable, to say no more of it, nor can I think that having no inclination for any but of one's own sex is enough to maintain such a character as I wish may still be yours.

This was thought a bit much even from a Duchess to a Queen.

On 30 July 1714, like her uncle Charles II, Anne rose 'finding herself pretty well', got her hair combed, had two fits and fell unconscious. Then like upon her uncle, seven doctors vented their enthusiasm: bleeding, cupping, clysters, emetics, hot irons, head shaved, garlic rubs. She lasted two days, amid three clerics itching for the closing ceremonies and to the annoyance of the famed Dr Mead, 'who pronounc'd several hours before that she could not live two minutes'. The post-mortem at Kensington Palace disclosed a small umbilical hernia (like Queen Victoria), no abdominal fluid, the organs normal, a small ulcer on the left leg. 'We can give no further account, being forbid making any other inspection than what was absolutely necessary for Embalming the Body,' apologised the seven physicians.

A lifetime of uterine patriotism, and no heir. They had to send to Hanover for George.

She concocted Queen Anne's Bounty for poor parsons. She struggled to pass the Occasional Conformity Act ('the only Act of its kind in History, until the Speed limit was invented'). She believed in the Royal Touch to cure scrofula, one of her patients being Dr Johnson, but it didn't work.

She was dull, dim, and devout, taciturn and evasive, her bad eyesight masked the arts, but she was a keen gardener. She overate, secretly drank brandy and (like most of the nobs) took laudanum. She gambled as incessantly as she prayed: 'Yesterday I won three hundred pounds but have lost almost half of it again this morning,' she mentioned in a letter to her dear friend Sarah. She was familiar with Newmarket, and paid a thousand guineas for a horse called Leeds.

Her passage through English history was decorated with the glorious tapestries of Blenheim, Ramillies, Oudenarde and Malplaquet and left some delightful architecture. 'Queen Anne was one of the smallest people ever set in a great place,' said Walter Bagehot. She exhibited the coming glory of the British crown: the irrelevance of its wearer.

$\mathcal{V}$ICTORIA

1819–1901

FRIDAY 6 MARCH 1891 was a busy day at Windsor Castle. The Queen had commanded there a performance of *The Gondoliers*. The operetta had been a crashing success at the Savoy Theatre for over a year, its first-night ovation overpowering the clattering traffic outside in the Strand. It had of course as little to do with Venice as *The Mikado* with Japan, and disquiet fluttered both sides of the Windsor curtain about some cheeky numbers which might leave Her Majesty unamused.

> *Oh, 'tis a glorious thing, I ween,*
> *To be a regular Royal Queen!*
> *No half-and-half affair, I mean,*
> *But a right-down regular Royal Queen!*

> *And everybody will roundly vow*
> *She's fair as flowers in May,*
> *And say, 'How clever!'*
> *At whatsoever*
> *She condescends to say!*

And so on.

On the Windsor programme, *The Gondoliers* was 'By Sir Arthur Sullivan'. W. S. Gilbert's name was nowhere, though the wig-maker got a credit in bold type. 'And I had to pay £87 10s as my share of sending the piece down to Windsor,' Gilbert complained 'besides forfeiting my share of the night's profits at the Savoy!' Perhaps the omission was an oversight: but he left the printer unthreatened, and Gilbert was a man who whistled up his solicitor as freely as another his dog. Our quarrelsome, gouty, bossy, busy Swift of the Savoy had to linger for fourteen years after Sir Arthur's knighthood, and until another reign, before he could kneel for his own—which he accepted as 'a tin-pot, twopenny-halfpenny sort of distinction.'

Queen Victoria's famously limited sense of humour excluded any light amusement reflected off herself. Whenever she jested there was the one about the lady who mistook her dinner-fork for her fan—everyone fell about, on the poet T. E. Brown's principle that 'a rich man's joke is always funny.' Nothing is more flattering to the powerful, the noble, and the moneymaking than the chortling implication that they are humorous as well—as the inescapable, and usually indigestible, after-dinner speech instructs us so often.

Flattery for the Queen was daily presented and consumed as normally as her breakfast. She disliked Gladstone—who, they said, if soaked, boiled, rinsed and twisted into a rope would not ooze a drop of fun—who orated, not conversed, and was too earnest for frivolous flattery. She loved Disraeli, who made little jokes and confessed to laying flattery on her with a trowel.

Queen Victoria's doctor over the last twenty years of her life, Sir James Reid, flattered her richly and valuably with unstinted professional devotion on miserable pay.

In the winter of 1899, the Queen wrote to him from Windsor to nearby Maidenhead: 'I am anxious to know if you would come over for an hour or two on Wednesday.'

It appeared that one of the household was undergoing delusions. She herself had a bad shoulder, she was suffering from the wind and not eating, and she was worrying about the war in South Africa. 'I have gone through so much anxiety that I am not surprised I should get bilious,' she lamented, though adding more cheerfully: 'The bowels are acting fully.'

Receiving such information by post was part of the doctor's duty, except that Sir James was enjoying the first week of his honeymoon.

Queens and their subjects are one flesh, but if everybody treats you as the most important person in the world—even, unthinkably! for their own ends—it is difficult to disagree with them.

Queen Victoria ascended the throne in 1837, turned eighteen. She was a well-built girl, under five feet tall and weighing nine stone, and her dresses were growing tighter. She was advised on her diet, as on everything else, by her fifty-eight-year old Prime Minister, Lord Melbourne. He banned mild ale and spicy dishes, recommending instead plenteous plain food with adequate wine, which Hanoverians like her thrived on. He told her to walk more, but this was unpopular.

Her first doctor was Sir James Clark, a Scotsman, a consumption specialist and enthusiast for fresh air, which he wanted to pump forcefully through Buckingham Palace. Early in 1839, he made a dreadful boob. A lady-in-waiting, thirty-two year old unmarried Lady Flora Hastings, fairy-faced with big eyes and lovely ringlets, consulted him about an enlarging abdomen and sickness. Clark prescribed camphor liniment and rhubarb pills.

The Court began to whisper, in the unkind way of all social classes, that Lady Flora was in the family way. The twenty-year-old unmarried Queen shot a glance, and agreed. Everyone knew that Lady Flora was intimate with Sir John Conroy, Comptroller of the Household of the Duchess of Kent, who was Victoria's mother, whom the Queen disdained. Conroy was a handsome, rapacious, raffish fellow, whom she hated. 'We have no doubt that she is—to use plain words—with *child*!!' the Queen logged with relish in her diary. 'The horrid cause of all this is the Monster & demon Incarnate.'

Clark unethically leaked the pregnancy diagnosis. The Queen informed Lord Melbourne and consulted the Duke of Wellington. The court bubbled, the newspapers nosed, Parliament bristled. Such lechery in the corridors of purity was horrifying. Melbourne summoned Clark. Was he right? They shrugged that they could only wait and see.

Clark had admittedly made the diagnosis through her dress. He wanted to examine her more carefully, without her stays. Lady Flora refused. Shedding clothes and modesty under the assumedly sexless eye of a male doctor had to wait until the next century.

Clark then told the patient herself she was pregnant. She demanded a second opinion. A specialist in women's diseases was consulted. He found her a virgin.

Lady Flora insisted the doctor give her a certificate. The scandal was now across Europe, duels were being threatened by her relatives, Clark was hounded to the sack, a vote against Melbourne and the Palace was paraded through Parliament, worse, the Queen was hissed at Ascot.

On 7 June, Lady Flora became ill, on 5 July she died at Buckingham Palace. Five thousand attended her funeral, weeping. She had insisted on a post-mortem—*not* by Clark—which revealed cancerous secondaries causing enlargement of her liver and fluid distending her abdomen. Clark consequently enjoyed hearty instruction in the medical journals on the differential diagnosis of a swelling female belly. The day that his patient had been maliciously calculated to give birth, Prince Albert arrived in England and put the poor woman from the Queen's mind for good.

Victoria's health over the first quarter-century of her reign was glowing, though Clark was commenting uneasily in 1856 on a 'morbid melancholy' striking the Queen's mind. 'Unless she is kept quiet and still amused, the time will come when she will be in danger,' he warned, but he thought the Prince Consort could handle it.

Clark survived until 1860, when he was followed by Dr William Baly, but he was killed in a railway accident at Wimbledon in January 1861. Then by Sir William Jenner, of University College Hospital, the fever expert who in 1847 first distinguished typhus fever, which is distributed by the louse, from typhoid fever, which comes in the drains. Sir William was short and fat, preferred to be carried from his front door to his brougham, and in 1898 created a professional record by leaving £375,000.

The Prince Consort shortly necessitated Jenner exercising his skills.

In November 1861, Albert took a chill—shivering, sleepless, aching, unable to shoot. By December, he was existing on raspberry vinegar in seltzer, with ether drops to sleep. Jenner diagnosed the slow fever—typhoid. Lord Palmerston, the Prime Minister, made his case more difficult by insisting that Jenner summoned more doctors, but by then Albert was delirious and had developed a paranoia against the entire medical profession.

Bulletins were issued, but so anodyne that Prince Edward, up at Cambridge, when summoned to Windsor on 13 December, stopped for a dinner party in London and arrived at three in the morning full of jollity and champagne. The patient was by then incoherent, listless and gasping, brandy was being administered half-hourly, the next evening he was dead.

The distraught Queen kissed his lips. She escaped infection through immunity enjoyed from an attack of typhoid, aged sixteen, caught at Ramsgate, the health resort on the Kent coast.

Typhoid was the malevolent goblin of the Royal Family. In a freezing November ten years later, the Prince of Wales, just turned thirty, took a fever at Sandringham and shortly became delirious and convinced that he already sat on the throne. The doctors, like Caesar's augurers at the ides of March, uttered prognostications which crushed the Queen into one of her depressions.

Jenner called reinforcement from Guy's Hospital: Sir William Withey Gull, the physician of the moment. He also was of Napoleonic frame, imperious, witty, an aphorist and pedagogue, a poetry-lover and scholar of the London sparrows. He proclaimed the uselessness of all the drugs which were then being applied lavishly to diseases of which the cure and the cause were equally unknown. 'His manner was the same in a hospital ward as in a palace,' they complimented the egalitarian, who in 1890 left £344,000 and during the next century was ludicrously accused of being Jack the Ripper.

Applying not drugs but 'masterly inactivity', Gull was able to inform the Queen smugly that no one had been known before to recover from typhoid who had been so ill as her son. In February 1872, Edward enjoyed a Thanksgiving Service at St Paul's, and how everyone cheered when the Queen kissed the convalescent's hand in her open carriage at Temple Bar! What a difference from Lady Flora.

Typhoid fever was one of three painful experiences by which Queen Victoria touched three fundamental advances in medicine, made in the second half of her reign in Germany, Scotland and America.

1. *Microbiology*.

The antics of Typhoid Mary, who scattered typhoid germs murderously round New York, were thirty years ahead. Nobody yet knew what caused typhoid. The fever was shudderingly blamed on miasmas arising from the ubiquitous foul-smelling gutters, drains, tenements, abattoirs, hospitals and urban rivers. 'Dr Condy's Fluid'—pink potassium permanganate—and eau-de-Cologne were poured lavishly to arrest the mysterious 'putrefactions' emitting the deadly 'contagia'.

Florence Nightingale in the Crimea abolished the stinks with scrubbing; Queen Victoria's sanitary knight, Edwin Chadwick beside the reeking Thames, constructed drains like railway tunnels to carry the scepter'd isle's excreta away upon its ebb tides. Meanwhile, the water closet was encroaching as usefully into civilised life as the gaslamp.

The microbial mystery was solved in 1880, when the pathologist Karl Joseph Eberth of Halle saw down his microscope the wriggly typhoid germ with its hairlike propellant flagella. This discovery opened twenty years as beneficial to the world as the voyage of the Ark. The microbes causing: gonorrhoea, leprosy, boils, septicaemia, childbed fever, tuberculosis, glanders, diphtheria, cholera, pneumonia, tetanus, diarrhoea, meningitis, gas-gangrene, and bubonic plague were all identified, mostly by orderly-minded Prussians. How Prince Albert would have been proud!

Ironically, he had himself just organised the clearing of Windsor Castle's fifty-three brimming cesspits, and replaced its ancient commodes with the 'Pedestal Vase' and the 'Closet of the Century', before he fell to mankind's yet undiscovered enemies. Nobody had any idea how to cure the diseases these newly found microbes caused for another four reigns, but even Professors Fleming and Florey had to start somewhere.

2. *Antiseipsis.*

On 4 August 1871, the Queen, at her summer residence of Osborne in the Isle of Wight, was stung on the elbow. Ten days later, she felt ill, lost her appetite, developed a sore throat. A regal row was progressing at the time. Prime Minister Gladstone wished the Queen to present herself more regularly to the people and to Parliament, both of which were becoming embarrassingly aware of being her paymasters, and not getting value for their money. The Emperor Napoleon III had that March been ejected from Paris to Chislehurst, republicanism was in the breeze which had carried him, freshening the cheeks of British abdicationists. She must stay down south until Parliament rose.

'The Queen is feeling extremely unwell,' she told him. He refused to swallow the stale excuse. Three days later, she took the royal train to her beloved residence of Balmoral, amid 'her faithful and ever-sympathetic Scotch subjects,' whom she much preferred to the vulgar English. The infection from the sting had spread. Her left arm was 'very painful'. Three days more, and she was 'suffering tortures'.

Sir William Jenner got the *Lancet* to print its opinion that London lay outside her medical limits. This incited mutterings that she hand over Buckingham Palace to her son. Jenner countered that nobody wanted to go to London except society gadflies. Why shouldn't the Queen enjoy her retirement? Why need she receive foreign ambassadors, 'a parcel of rubbishy old people trying to make something to do?' Anyway, the Queen had only twenty-four hours to live, he closed the argument.

On 23 August, Jenner discovered that she had an abscess in her left armpit, though he was perplexed what sort it was. On 3 September, the Queen was so ill that Jenner summoned the Professor of Surgery from Edinburgh, Joseph

Lister. He arrived with his donkey engine beside him in the carriage.

If you escaped from surgery with your life, you were generally killed promptly by hospital gangrene. This was inflicted by the streptococcus and staphylococcus, but you had to wait until 1880 for Pasteur to find out. In 1865, when Lister was Professor at Glasgow, Pasteur had already shown that something invisible in the air ruined the French wine. Lister, a wine-merchant's son, suspected that this invisible something, as solid as the dust on the piano, rotted his surgical wounds. He would exterminate it with pungent carbolic acid, which he had noticed removed the stink from the Carlisle sewage just over the border.

Lister first tried carbolic on Jimmy Greenlees, aged eleven with a compound fractured tibia, then six years later on the Queen. He had applied crude carbolic-and-lint dressings, then carbolic plaster and carbolic putty, then a one in twenty dilution from his donkey engine, which was three-foot high and sprayed forcefully wound, dressing, instruments and surgeon's finger-tips.

The abscess bursting from the Queen's left armpit was thought by her Household terribly undignifed, the blight of charwomen and laundresses. The Queen in her bed complained testily that she had to wait half an hour while Lister discussed it outside with Jenner. Lister said he must cut at once. Sir William fuddled the Queen with a whiff of chloroform, Lister froze the pointing red skin with ethyl chloride, and the local GP was on the donkey engine, which he had not seen before in his life.

Knife! Carbolic! The GP pumped, and hit the Queen in the face. Such aim, inexcusable in the butts, infuriated the semi-conscious monarch. In the horrified glare of his colleagues, the GP could but mumble, 'that he was only the man who works the bellows', like Nero protesting that he was only playing the fiddle. Lister cut. Pus spurted. 'In an instant there was relief,' said the Queen. Next morning: 'Had a cup of coffee before the terrible long dressing of the wound took place. Mr Lister's great invention, a carbolic spray to destroy all organic germs, was used before the bandages were removed, and during the dressing.' So she bestowed a merited accolade.

The wound not draining freely, Lister displayed the admirable improvisation of the surgical profession by detaching the rubber tube between the carbolic and the atomiser of his donkey engine, cutting it into short bits and inserting them into the Queen's armpit. Thus she inaugurated a technique of drainage which persisted until antibiotics made 'laudable pus' from a healing wound a Victorian relic.

3. *Anaesthesia*.

The Queen's third brush with medical progress had already occurred, on 7 April 1853. Anaesthesia wafted into the world at the Massachusetts General Hospital in Boston, where William Morton gave ether on 16 October 1846. Next year, Sir James Young Simpson, Professor of Midwifery at Edinburgh, displayed chloroform by passing it round a dinner-party and putting his guests under the table. Chloroform was swifter and sweeter than ether, just the stuff for labour pains. The pious thence enjoyed the delicious outrage of indicating that this contradicted the directions in Genesis, to bring forth children in sorrow. The pious were all males, who ignored God's mercifully anaesthetising Adam before falling upon his ribs.

'Medical men may oppose for a time the superinduction of anaesthesia in parturition,' Simpson saw sensibly in 1847, 'but they will oppose it in vain; for certainly our patients themselves will force the use of it upon the profession. The whole question is, even now, one merely of time.'

The time came on 7 April 1853, when the Queen—who had discretely inquired about chloroform for the birth of Prince Arthur in 1850—took it from England's anaesthetic herald, Dr John Snow, for the birth of Prince Leopold. Leopold was the eighth of nine children born over seventeen years, between ten months after her wedding and four years before the expiry of Albert. The Queen had an ounce of chloroform, dripped on a handkerchief over fifty-three minutes, enough to keep her woozy. 'Blessed chloroform, soothing quietening and delightful beyond measure,' the experienced mother endorsed anaesthesia, which became so popular that it was bestowed as a name upon hapless newborn children.

Sir James Reid was a nondescript Aberdeen GP who applied himself like a kaolin poultice to the Queen from 1881 until her death. He had ventured to Vienna and spoke German, echoing poor Albert. He was thirty-one, pink, gingery and bristly, with confluent side-whiskers and moustache and a perky pince-nez. He was paid £400 a year—the equivalent of £20,000 in this age when the Queen's Chief Medical Officer collects £87,435. He would be in constant attendance on the Queen, except for six weeks' leave (which she interrupted postally pitilessly). He was in charge of all Scotch servants, including the awful kilted sex symbol John Brown, who fortunately died in his care two years later, and Reid stepped respectably into his brogues.

Doctors ranked socially in Victoria's opinion below cavalry officers. Reid's place was laid out: he was *not* an official member of the Royal Household, he could take breakfast and lunch with the ladies and gentlemen in waiting *but not dinner*. Except at Balmoral, where nobody cared. He was later allowed the gold buttons and braid of the Household uniform, even the envied Windsor uniform, which flashed scarlet at collar and cuffs. Reid attended also to paramedical matters, like the disposal of the Queen's dog—whose death had necessitated strengthening her sleeping-draught and his presence at her bedside until 1 a.m.—and whose burial called for a lead-lined, charcoal-stuffed coffin, a bag of coins, a brick-lined grave and its replica in bronze.

The Queen held her daily consultation with Reid at about midnight, in case of extra medication to endure the night. He usually gave her bromide, hyoscine and opium. Whenever she woke, and however often, her ring roused her maids. Unthinking inconsideration for all about you is a trying royal prerogative.

Attacks of indigestion, wind and colic could keep Reid at her bedside until 5.30 a.m. He ascribed these to overeating, and tried replacing her usual diet with Benger's Food, but she ate both.

The Queen enjoyed claret and Scotch so impartially that she mixed them together in her glass. She suffered rheumaticky aches, for which a masseuse was imported from Aix-les-Bains, and attacks of nerves induced equally devastatingly by the bellicosity of nations or the squabbles of her family. She had bad teeth but refused to see dentists and ended with false ones. She had bad eyes but refused to wear glasses. She had also a hernia and a uterine prolapse, which Reid was unaware of, as he never saw her with her clothes off.

Subservience and intimacy elevated Reid to a baronetcy and an informal, but feared, influence at Court more intellectually effective than John Brown's, whose lock of hair and photograph he was charged to slip secretly into the Queen's left hand when she lay in a coffin lined with lead and crammed with charcoal, like her dog's.

Kings and queens, princes and princesses, though no more intelligent than their brighter subjects, only better informed, become fleshed deities for whom politicians can invite their countrymen to die, who are acclaimed in the streets and at the races, who are utilised to open Parliaments or hospitals, and who enhance the menus of dinners or the swirl of balls with their gracious presence. They are demonstrations of practical genetics, being bred to induce and accept this singular veneration.

Another century, and our rulers, our great statesmen, our magnificent pianists, our poets, English batsmen and American pitchers, will all be created by genetic engineering. There is a shining precedent in the House of Lords.

> The House of Peers, throughout the war,
> Did nothing in particular,
> And did it very well,

Gilbert noted admiringly the House's discreet effectiveness. This hereditary House—exclusively, until unbred Lords were admitted in 1958—is ahead of its time as the only genetically engineered legislative body in the world. And this was achieved, since the Norman *curia regis* of 1066, not through microscopical fiddling, but by means which even their lowliest underlings found most agreeable.

$\mathscr{F}$REDERICK III

1831–1888

GENERAL CARL VON CLAUSEWITZ's remark: 'War is the continuation of politics by other means', has painfully become trite. It was made in his battle-scarred philosophy *On War*, published in Berlin the year after his death from cholera in 1831.

Europe of 1887 was sophisticated about this principle.

Traditional wars had been kings' wars, all fluttering flags and beating drums, fought between paid or press-ganged troops in beautifully braided uniforms. The victors abducted a province or two, the defeated went home, the citizens of both meanwhile mingled as peaceful travellers. *Mais nous avons changé tout cela*, Napoleon could have quoted Molière. Observed von Clausewitz: 'Buonaparte's military power, based on the strength of the whole nation, marched over Europe, smashing everything in pieces so surely and certainly, that where it only encountered the old-fashioned Armies the result was not doubtful for a moment. A reaction, however, awoke in time. War became of itself an affair of the people.'

Politicians conscripted their nations, reminding them of Horace's *Dulce et decorum est pro patria mori*. Firearms now turned a man into a soldier as quickly as he could learn to aim. An efficient military machine could grab what the admittedly far less expensive diplomats failed to. If the politicians won the war, they became national heroes with beautiful girls scattering rose petals before their triumphant carriages, like Hitler in 1940. If the war machine was smashed, they saw a good bet lost and sought obscurity in exile, or in Hell, like Hitler in 1945.

In 1887 Great Britain ruled the waves and it was Queen

Victoria's Jubilee. France was enjoying the third Republic and the later Impressionists. Chancellor Bismarck had consolidated the German Empire, nationalised the railways, created a tobacco monopoly, raised tariffs, repressed socialism and strengthened the army. By 'other means', his politics had efficiently solved the difficult Schleswig-Holstein question in 1864 then settled uppish Austria and quarrelsome Napoleon III. The German Emperor William I was ninety. The socialists had tried to assassinate him thrice, and he was enthusiastic about strengthening the army.

William's only son Prince Frederick William ('Fritz') came to London to see the Great Exhibition in 1851, aged twenty, and took a fancy to the Princess Royal, Victoria ('Pussy'), aged ten. The relationship was encouraged by Queen Victoria and Albert, to achieve the stability of Europe. Fritz was blue-eyed with a new moustache, friendly, unaffected, liberal-minded, peaceful, a man born to attenuate the army. Fritz visited Balmoral in 1855, shot a stag and asked for Pussy's hand. Her parents were delighted. The couple were permitted to kiss.

The German demand for the marriage to be held in Berlin was rejected as an insult. The bridegroom's family, the Hohenzollerns, were tediously coarse. The vast dinner at Buckingham Palace sparkled with diamonds like fireworks, and at the Chapel Royal in St James's Mr Mendelssohn contributed a rousing Wedding March. The bride was seventeen, and a haemophilia carrier.

'Vicky' took up her duties as Crown Princess of Germany. Her mother took up her pen, daily. A year after her wedding Vicky had a son, a difficult breech delivery, his left arm dislocated during labour. The future Kaiser William II ('Willy'), with the upswept moustaches, pickelhaube and paralysed arm, had turned twenty-eight when his father first sought treatment for hoarseness.

Crown Prince Frederick, who now had a beard, took a drive from the Neues Palais at Potsdam in January without his overcoat, the coachman got lost, it grew dark and cold, circumstances shortly necessitating the summoning of throat specialist Professor Gerhardt from Berlin.

The Professor numbed Frederick's throat with cocaine, flashed his little mirror and saw a lump on the left vocal cord in the larynx.

He tried lassoing it with a wire, then fiddled with a scalpel, then frizzled it for a fortnight with his electric cautery. The wound bled, the lump stayed. The Professor, an expert on paralysis of the vocal cords, rejected cancer because both cords moved. Like all experts, if they are wrong they must be fundamentally wrong. He recommended a couple of weeks amid the hot springs at Baden-Baden.

In May, the Professor decided to operate, by proxy. He brought from Berlin Professor Ernst von Bergmann, ex-Prussian Army, a cranial surgeon who introduced steam sterilisers and modern asepsis. They would split open the Adam's apple and have a good look. Theatre equipment and nurses were smuggled from the Charité Hospital in Berlin to the palace (which did not run to bathrooms). The Prince would be chloroformed at seven on Saturday morning, 21 May, though nobody had yet been told, including the Emperor and the patient.

Bismarck found out. The difficulties of the Crown Prince's larynx henceforth became the difficulties of Europe.

Bismarck furiously threw into the surgical battle a hand-picked squad of four doctors, one the Medical Director of the German Army. The bugle blew in Buckingham Palace. Frantic cipher telegrams from Vicky alerted Queen Victoria that they were going to cut the throat of *unser Fritz*. She implored the Queen to dispatch England's dashing laryngeal cavalier, Morell Mackenzie. 'We cannot bear to think of poor darling Vicky's anguish and sorrow', proclaimed the Queen, and that night Dr Mackenzie was galloping on his way from Harley Street.

Mackenzie had founded the popular throat Hospital in Golden Square, Soho, in 1863. Attending his private practice necessitated tipping the butler to avoid two hours' squatting in his gilt-pillared waiting-room. He had written *Diseases of the Throat* and *On Enlarged Tonsils and their Treatment Without Cutting* (cutting was performed at the time unanaesthetised, sitting up in a high chair). He was a Scot born in the East End of London, sharp-nosed, neatly side-whiskered, addicted to stramonium cigarettes for his asthma, smug, flamboyant, rich, moving among Irving, Tree, Pinero and Whistler, and disliked by the medical profession.

At Potsdam, Mackenzie plucked a specimen from the larynx,

pronounced no cancer and cancelled the operation. His happy diagnosis was confirmed in Berlin by the world-famous pathologist and anti-Bismarck Member of the Reichatag, Rudolph Virchow. The palace doctors were demobilised. Fritz gratefully recommended Mackenzie for a knighthood, which he received at Balmoral, after lunch. The Queen had jibbed, but to refuse would surely shed a depressing shadow of doubt on the prognosis.

In June, Fritz came for the Jubilee, still husky. Mackenzie picked more bits off his vocal cord. The Prince decided to heal his wounds by wintering in the city of flowers, renting the Villa Zirio in San Remo on the Italian Riviera. Willy appeared at the villa, insisting angrily that his father return to Berlin, because the Emperor might die any minute. Queen Victoria forbade the move north. The sicker the Emperor, the healthier Fritz must become to succeed him.

In early November, Mackenzie was back with his patient.

The weather was too cold for the Prince to go out. A telegram of encouragement had arrived, signed by 180,000 in Berlin. The lump had spread to the right vocal cord.

'Is it cancer?' whispered the Prince.

'I am sorry to say, sir, that it looks very much like it.'

Fritz gave a wan smile. 'Under the circumstances I really must apologise for feeling so well.'

Mackenzie had unfortunately compounded his wrong diagnosis by missing his target, and plucking for Professor Virchow a speck of normal laryngeal tissue.

A regiment of doctors marched from Berlin and Vienna. Mackenzie reinforced himself with Dr Hovell from Golden Square. There was a truce in the attack. Perhaps it was not cancer at all, but syphilis? *Unser Fritz* had collected a dose in 1869. It was all the fault of the Suez Canal. At its gala opening by the Empress Eugénie, Fritz had celebrated the absence of Vicky with the lovely Spanish Dolores Cada, and shortly appeared with a penile chancre before the Khedive's physician. As Dr von Wassermann's handy diagnostic reaction lay forty years ahead, Fritz's doctors could but fill him up with the current (ineffective) treatment of potassium iodide, and hope that the laryngeal lump would disappear. It did not. Mackenzie needed to appraise Vicky of the earlier diagnosis, and got his face slapped.

Willy now entered the attack. He enlisted doctor number thirteen, and put them all on parade. Mackenzie said Fritz had eighteen months to live. The Germans said six. 'I thought Mackenzie would die of shame! But his face, which I was watching narrowly, showed no trace of emotion,' reflected Willy, ordering dismiss.

They decided to operate. Mackenzie complained that the Germans' policy was 'kill or cure': if they tried an elaborate laryngectomy, it would turn them from surgeons into assassins. But a simple tracheostomy hole would serve so long as there was breath in the Prince's body. They left it to the patient. Fritz chose the second. He was the calmest man present.

The operation was performed on 9 February 1888, in the drawing-room, by five doctors. Dr Bramann of San Remo did the cutting, because he handled children choking from diphtheria. Dr Mackenzie was on the pulse and Dr Hovell on the chloroform. A vivid picture of the operation was swiftly printed in Cologne, and immediately banned 'by order from the highest authority'—probably Willy. The doctors were next commanded by Willy to sign a secret document giving the clinical truth, which was instantly leaked to the Berlin papers. Two more doctors then turned up at San Remo, making fifteen.

The German press, who anticipated our *paparazzi* by surrounding the villa Zirio with telescopes, hated Morell Mackenzie as an English surgical instrument (though he was, they hinted, really Moritz Markovicz, a Polish Jew). The German doctors hated him because he was haughty and independent, while they were all State servants trembling at the sack if they upset anyone. The Germans in general hated Vicky as *die Engländerin*, a woman solicitous to keep her husband alive until she could enjoy a fatter Empress' pension, that she might marry her Chamberlain, Count Seckendorff, who everybody knew was her lover. Willy hated his mother because, being English, she gave him an inferiority complex, which he overreacted against.

There was muttering in the beer-gardens about applying the

Salic Law—which excluded women from the throne—to sickly Hohenzollerns, and making Willy an instant Emperor. Bismarck was anyway considering proclaiming him Regent, if his grandfather predeceased his father. Willy's pride and arrogance was inflated by Bismarck's already empowering him to sign State papers, as 'Prince of Prussia'. William I died on 9 March. Fritz became Emperor, voiceless, dying, gentle, dutifully reporting to Berlin by train through the snowbound Alps, which everyone said Bismarck hoped would kill him.

The breathing aperture into his trachea needed a short curved cannula, an item of Anglo-German contention. The German doctors grudgingly agreed that Mackenzie's own cannula was less irritating, but none of them being laryngologists they bungled its insertion, made the patient bleed, and left in a huff.

In April, Mackenzie diplomatically invited Professor von Bergmann to insert his new tube, but the Professor at five in the afternoon was swaying drunk and poked it into the neck muscles, the patient turned blue and nearly died. Von Bergmann—not really a 'von' but a Slav from Riga—was dishonourably discharged, but it was *die Engländerin* and her doctor whom the German press vitriolically attacked for the disaster. A professor from the Charité and four colleagues now arrived at the palace, bringing the strength of the medical garrison to twenty.

On 22 April, Queen Victoria arrived to see what was going on. 'That was a woman!' Bismarck assessed, after meeting her. She told Willy not to be a naughty boy. On 15 June, Fritz started coughing up the cartilage rings of his windpipe, and died from bronchopneumonia after ninety-three days as Emperor Frederick III. Willy, now Emperor William II, instantly made a fuss, posting armed guards and patrols of hussars, forbidding anyone to leave or send a wire on pain of instant arrest. He insisted through his mother's tears on a post-mortem, which continued the doctors' policy of outnumbering the patient by involving ten of them.

Fritz's motto was *Lerne zu leiden ohne zu klagen*. We must learn to suffer without complaint. It was sad, but it is oft-tested, and it is of the holiest precedent.

Mackenzie returned to Harley Street with a £12,000 fee and

wrote *The Fatal Illness of Frederick the Noble*, which sold 100,000 copies, also 100,000 in Germany, but Willy had the police confisicate the lot on publication day. The German doctors published *Die Krankheit Kaiser Friedrich des Dritten*. The German Foreign Minister, who was Bismarck's son, pronounced that, but for the disaster of encountering Mackenzie, Frederick would have lived for years. Both sides accused the other of malpractice and misconduct, libel writs were scattered like bloody swabs, even the Royal Colleges of Surgeons and Physicians turned vengefully righteous towards unpopular Mackenzie. Four years, and he was dead.

Willy's policy was strengthening the army.

We belong to each other, I and the army. We were born for each other and will cleave indissolubly to each other, whether it be the will of God to send us calm or storm. From the world above, the eyes of my forefathers look down upon me, that I shall one day have to stand accountable to them for the glory and honour of the army,

he declared with a lover's passion.

The British and German politics of economic and colonial expansion turned from competition to confrontation, then to combat. Had Frederick III lived as long as William I, Europe's political sheep might have grazed thirty years in peace. Though Willy was not all to blame:

No people has ever with greater brutality better prepared its economic conquests with the sword, and later ruthlessly defended them, than the English nation. Is it not positively the distinguishing feature of British statesmanship to draw economic acquisitions from political strength, and at once to recast every gain in economic strength into political power? And what an error to believe that England is personally too much of a coward to stake her own blood for her economic policy! The fact that the English people possessed no 'people's army' in no way proved the contrary . . . She fought with mercenaries as long as mercenaries sufficed; but she reached down into the precious

blood of the whole nation when only such a sacrifice could
bring victory; but the determination for victory, then tenacity
and ruthless pursuit of this struggle, remained unchanged,

admiringly wrote Willy's Nazi successor as the head of German
military power in 1925. So we had two European wars, both won
by the Americans, until the H-Bomb made von Clausewitz read like
a fairy-tale.

LITERARY

JAMES BOSWELL

1740–1795

Mr ANDREW DOUGLAS was a Scotsman, a former Naval surgeon who became a smart practitioner in Pall Mall in London, and who had learnt his job by apprenticeship.

As ordinary men are descended from monkeys, so surgeons have evolved from barbers. Attendants with sharp instruments in their fingers wearied of scraping the surface of their work, and elaborated the accidental bloody nick into a deliberate severance of the veins, letting the blood therapeutically (according to their lights) into neat pewter bowls flattened along one side to nuzzle against the flesh. Only those barbers adept at blood-letting could survive, like the fiches on the Galapagos Islands blessed with beaks strong enough to crack the nuts. An illustration of Darwinian principles (possibly).

In 1505, the venturesome barbers of Edinburgh were cutting into their customers deeply enough to feel that their abilities merited respect. They petitioned the Town Council for a 'Seal of Cause', granted by James IV to create the Incorporation of Barber Surgeons. This guild enjoyed in Edinburgh the valuable monopolies of both surgery and of making and selling whisky. It received one executed criminal per year for dissection, its candidates were examined in anatomy and the signs of the Zodiac, needed to read and write, were charged £5 entrance fee and had to stand all the other members dinner.

As the Institute was not magnified into the Royal College of Surgeons of Edinburgh until 1778, academic rigours did not tax Mr Douglas, who mastered his craft, as did the lather boy, at his master's elbow. Like his contemporary William Smellie, the exponent of the wooden midwifery forceps, he had appreciated with

Samuel Johnson that 'the noblest prospect which a Scotchman ever sees, is the high road that leads him to England.'

On Friday, 19 November 1762, James Boswell, a friend over the past two years, arrived unexpectedly at Andrew Douglas' door. Boswell was the eldest son of Lord Auchinleck, himself the son of a lawyer, a crushingly important Edinburgh judge. Boswell's child-hood home lay in the minatory shadow of the Edinburgh Court House, his education in the moral chill of tutors aspiring to be ministers of the Church of Scotland. At thirteen, he entered the University of Edinburgh to study classics, then the University of Glasgow to study law, his father regally assuming that he would perpetuate the occupational dynasty.

Boswell was a 'greeting bairn', snivelling, scared of the dark, terrified of ghosts, shy and spotty. He grew into a 'tim'rous laddie', gloomy, swarthy and fat, but with the ripening of his endocrines flowered into a witty, vain, convivial socialite, enthusiastically hedonistic and perseveringly randy. He discovered a literary talent, a knack for versifying, he was published in *The Scots Magazine*, he became magnetised by the stage, produced a play and intended to marry Mrs Cowper out of the cast, items affecting his father with equal outrage.

Edinburgh society was divided into the crammed wynds—the location of poverty, crime, disease and gardy-loo—and the genteel classes, modest, scholarly, pious, priggish, Presbyterian, snug, well if stodgily fed. Emphatically to avoid this, Boswell aged nineteen fled to London and became a Roman Catholic. He was received into the Church at the Bavarian Chapel in Soho. He was going to be a monk in France. But the plan was dropped, on discovery of a further talent for ingratiating himself with the great, which achieved him immortality.

Boswell was warmly welcomed in literary and libertine London. He rocketed through society and sought a commission in the Guards. Father demanded him home after three months, fuming in his frustration over disinheriting the family disgrace (alas, the family money belonged to his wife Euphemia, who at marriage had settled it on the unborn eldest). Lord Auchinleck hit on the solution. Marriage! The pressingly eligible young ladies of Edinburgh took tea and baps with Boswell round the drawing-room fire that winter, and though he professed himself wildly in love with several of them, his heart was not in it. He preferred less formal sexual encounters, copulating with the servant-girls in the attic to the extent of fathering the child of Peggy Doig, whom he obliterated from his life by giving her £10 to cover her costs.

With professional craftiness, Lord Auchinleck had his son acknowledge the authority of trustees—chosen by father—in return for £100 a year, which was enough to let him live beyond the embarrassment of his family. Boswell readily signed the deed. Anything to escape again to London.

He arrived by chaise that November Friday in 1762, after a journey of four days costing £11. He had stopped to bow thrice in farewell to Arthur's Seat, and on sighting London from Highgate Hill burst into cheers, song and extemporary poetry. His companion, a sea-captain, was bemused: London was simply the place he went for his orders from the East India Company. The bustle, the crowds, the glittering shops, the flaring lights excited Boswell more than ever. He booked into the Black Lion Inn off Fleet Street, dined, washed and shaved, and called on Mr Douglas in Pall Mall. The barber surgeon now had a fashionable practice, including the sporty Earl of Eglington in Mayfair, who had so rewardingly initiated Boswell into London society.

The welcome was gratifyingly warm. Douglas was 'a kind-hearted, plain, sensible man', his son was a scholar at Westminster, but his wife was one of those dreadful women who talk too much: 'very lively without much wit', Boswell grumbled, and often to be encountered in England. Douglas insisted he stay. They sat down to a hearty English dinner, Boswell recalling the soundness of the surgeon's table. Next morning, Boswell moved into his own dining-room and bedroom at the Douglas', calculating that rent-free he had enough money to live like a gentleman. Unfortunately, a week of Mrs Douglas was intolerable. He shifted to Downing Street, up two pair of stairs, use of the parlour in the morning, forty guineas a year and a shilling to dine with the family.

As Boswell began circulating delightedly round the gossipy coffee-houses and chop-houses of London, the urge which drove him to urinary ruin impelled him to seek old flames—Jeany Wells in Soho, Sally Forrester of the Blue Periwig Inn, 'my first lady of Venus's Bedchamber'—but they had flickered out. He sought a girl he had known in Edinburgh, but she was not having any. He picked up a tart in the Strand, who paid him a professional compliment upon his size, that if he ever took a girl's maidenhead he would make her squeak. He was wisely going to enjoy her in 'armour', the prototype condom made of linen or of sheep's gut, tied on with a ribbon which could be ordered in regimental colours. But she was unequipped with this tool of her trade, so he fiddled with her instead, gave her a shilling and shuddered all night at a risk so chancily shunned.

Boswell had already suffered two attacks of gonorrhoea: one from his first whore in London—dreadfully bad luck—which lasted ten weeks, then he 'catch'd a Tartar' in Edinburgh. He now determined resolutely to abjure whores and to find some reliably uninfective woman of fashion.

Safety was embodied in Mrs Anne Lewis, an actress, the Queen in *Hamlet* at Covent Garden Theatre, lovely, aged twenty-four, split from her actor husband. After a month's businesslike wooing, Boswell again booked into the Black Lion Inn, as Mr Digges, cousin of his lookalike who had stayed there. It was a voluptuous night of supreme rapture. He performed five times, three more than any man had achieved with her before—information perhaps more foreboding than flattering.

A week later, he felt a warmth in his penis, 'a symptom of that distemper with which Venus, when cross, takes it into her head to plague her votaries.' Next day it was hotter, the next he had a discharge and recognised that Signor Gonorrhoea had again come to stay. He boiled with anger. How could he possibly have caught it from the respectable Mrs Lewis? He called on her, inquiring acidly about her health. She paled and trembled. She certainly had *not* suffered the clap! Well, not for fifteen months. Unhappily, the gonococcus, like Sleeping Beauty, is startlingly awakened by a lover's kiss. Boswell withdrew with martyred dignity. He had been so looking forward to a winter's safe copulation. He remembered that he had lent her two guineas, and asked for them back.

He took his illness to 'my friend Douglas, whom I knew to be skillful and careful'. A quack, or self-medication—sulphurated pills at 2s 8d, mercurial pills at sixpence—would have been cheaper, but Boswell sensibly decided that health was of supreme importance, and more hopefully that he could save on other things. He called at Pall Mall for breakfast on 20 January 1763. Mrs Douglas rabbited on about Congreve, who lived with the old Lord Godolphin, and who had a daughter by crazy Lady Godolphin, while her husband was two years abroad, and Lord Godolphin allowed her, after Congreve's death, to keep a wax image of him in her bedchamber, which she talked to in the belief it was Congreve . . .

Boswell squirmed patiently over the coffee. She withdrew. He told the surgeon his sad story. Douglas was familiar with the case, having treated Boswell's first attack. He examined the affected parts and diagnosed a gonorrhoeal infection, which the woman must certainly have known she was passing. Boswell made a little joke. Would he take an IOU for his fees? And compress his treatment into but few visits, that he might have less to pay? The jokes did not go over. Douglas gravely prescribed treatment—rest, confinement, a meagre diet, purgatives, blood-letting—and charged five guineas. Boswell had faintly hoped for it free. He reflected that a man as your friend and a man as your surgeon have opposite characters. As a friend, Douglas was kind, anxious for his welfare, a ready host. As a surgeon, he wanted to keep him long and profitably under his care. 'I have to do not with him but his profession,' Boswell differentiated sombrely.

Boswell circulated round his social circle that he was going to the country, and stayed in his Downing Street room. He passed feverish nights, suffered pain in his left testicle, worried that it was swelling again, like it did in the Tartar. He dreamt of Douglas at his bedside, complaining it was a damned difficult case. He glimpsed death.

The gleet dribbled away, and after six weeks almost stopped. Douglas discharged him from further treatment and payment. They could be friends again. On 22 March, Boswell was invited to watch from Douglas' Pall Mall windows the procession of Heralds to the City to proclaim the end of the Seven Years War. On 25 March, he indicated his complete recovery by picking up a prostitute in St James's Park.

Boswell had another sixteen attacks of clap. He caught it in London, Rome, Venice, Edinburgh and Dublin. Douglas treated the tenth, from nightly intercourse with prostitutes over the weekend of 29 March to 1 April 1776. The latest treatment was irrigation of the urinary tract leading from the bladder with vitriol, nitrous acid, mercury salts and lead, all squirted down the penis. Chasteningly painful. A stricture of the urethra became inevitable, making it an effort to pee. This was treated by repeated 'sounding', dilatation of the urethra by long curved, tapered metal rods, slipped up the penis with a skill reaped from innumerable cases. Boswell was sounded in Hanover Square by Sir James Earle, the famed, deft lithotomist from Bart's. It almost made him faint, but he accepted an invitation to dinner.

Sir John Pringle, an expert in military medicine, another Edinburgh exile and friend of the recidivistic patient, provided him with the advice: 'I hope you have sincerely repented of that action (viz., gonorrhoea contracted from the 'common girl' while drunk). If you have not repented, and with great compunction, too, be assured that your misfortunes are not at an end.' The warning had no prophylactic effect. The vertiginous sounding had been performed shortly after Boswell's arrest by the watch for being drunk and disorderly. Six months later, he had recovered sufficiently to get drunk at Lord Lonsdale's, copulate with three prostitutes during a single day, and collect another dose.

Thirty-two years after his voluptuous night with Mrs Lewis, Boswell was carried home from a dinner of Johnson's Literary Club with acute urinary retention from a prostatic abscess. His final practitioner, Dr Richard Warren, breezed in with 'the pleasing assurance that his sufferings are nearly at an end'. Unfortunately, they were. Boswell died of kidney failure five days later. He left twelve children, five of them illegitimate.

How refreshing in these prying days to discover a distinguished literary figure of the past who was definitely not a homosexual.

$\mathscr{A}$LEXANDER $\mathscr{P}$OPE

1688–1744

EXQUISITELY twisted lines from a twisted frame.

> *The Muse but serv'd to ease some friend, not wife,*
> *To help me thro' this long disease, my life.*

Pope aged twelve contracted tuberculosis of the spine. This disease was sorted out eighty years later by Percival Pott, the pedagogic surgeon at Bart's, and bequeathed to the world as 'Pott's disease' (his own broken tibia, sustained riding in the Old Kent Road, was endowed as 'Pott's fracture', and an infective lump on the cranium became forever 'Pott's puffy tumour').

TB of any bone was common, incurred from drinking the widespread infected milk. In the spine, the round bodies of four or five vertebrae, in front of the spinal cord, became rarefied and collapsed, while the joints which arched behind the cord held the spine together. The infection left Pope with a permanent forward kink in his middle spine, his bowed head forcing him to look always upwards. He was 'about four foot six high, very hump-backed and deformed. He had a very large and very fine eye,' recorded the expert glance of Sir Joshua Reynolds.

Pope's legs were wasted, standing was tedious, and he felt the cold. He wore three pairs of stockings and a fur doublet, with a canvas jacket to keep him upright. He needed dressing and undressing, travelled uncomfortably on rough roads in bumpy coaches, and enjoyed no sexual activity—though the urethral stricture which he had painfully dilated aged fifty-two (like Boswell's) may betoken an earlier attack of gonorrhea from some Dunciad fling.

Alexander Pope was born in the nub of the City of London at Lombard Street, haunt of moneylenders. His father Alexander was forty-six, a prosperous linen-draper at the door of retirement; his mother Editha, a second wife, was pushing the menopause. They were Catholics. It was a bad year for young Alexander to join English history. In 1688, James II fled the country, William and Mary were about to impinge upon it, and Catholicism, after its shuddering swings under the Tudors and Stuarts had become an indubitably unEnglish activity.

New laws drove the Pope family from London to the village of Binfield beyond Windsor forest. When young Alexander fell ill, the family ascribed it to overwork, removed him from school, and consulted Dr John Radcliffe—none better! This arrogant man, medical master of both Whigs and Tories, made twenty guineas a day in London and posthumously decorated Oxford, amid the echoes of Latin oratory, with the Radcliffe Camera and the Radcliffe Library, also with the Radcliffe Infirmary down the road, all three still going strong. Dr Radcliffe treated Alexander with daily rides in the forest.

Grown into 'the wicked wasp of Twickenham' (Lady Mary Wortley Montagu's sting), Pope suffered in his riverside home lifelong headaches and depression, with attacks of vomiting and indigestion which he fancied he improved by drinking quantities of coffee, and feared that he aggravated by an indulgence in potted lampreys. His 'crazy carcass' provided plentiful employment for doctors, three or four at a time. Some of his treatment was imaginative: pain in his side provoked 'a course of brickbats and tiles, which they apply to me piping hot, morning and night; and sure it is very satisfactory to one who loves architecture at his heart to be built round in his very bed. My body may properly at this time be called a human structure.'

The patient changed his doctors often, or sought fashionable charlatans, with whom they were generally indistinguishable. Pope's favourite was Joshua 'Spot' Ward ('Spot' from the red birthmark on the left of his face), the loudest quack of the century.

In 1717 Ward, aged thirty-two, a Hackney drysalter who handled drugs, dyes, pickles and preserved meats, was elected MP for Marlborough, though nobody had voted for him. This discrepancy was discovered by Parliament to arise from forgery of the mayor's signature on the electoral return. Ward was expelled from the House. On 17 March 1727, he stood in the pillory. He was already worth £200,000, and had inaugurated some complicated shiftiness to salvage £50,000 of the South Sea Company's chairman's money, forfeited by a furious Commons after the crash in 1720. Ward cautiously slipped his own fortune to relatives, risking his neck by not revealing as much to the Court of Chancery. He was sent to prison, where 'his amusement was to give poison to dogs and cats and see them expire by slower or quicker torments'. Released, he fled to France and invented his pill.

> *Of late, without the least pretence to skill,*
> *Ward's grown a famed physician by a pill,*

Pope noticed.

Ward returned to England in 1733, and achieved a pardon from George II. He had spotted, in defiance of the Royal College of Physicians' diagnosis, that His Majesty was suffering not from a gouty, but a dislocated thumb, which Ward instantly, if painfully, reduced, earning an agonised royal kick on the shins and subsequent gratitude. He was given a coach and six with the right to drive it through St James's Park, and was specifically excluded by Parliament from the Apothecaries Act of 1748, which was passed to stop quacks like him peddling pills like his. The indulgence of British royalty towards useless remedies still shines warmly upon their purveyors.

Everyone took Ward's pill for everything. If you could not swallow pills, it came as 'the Drop'. Its secret ingredient was antimony, the infallible emetic. Mrs Gilbert, who kept the Horseshoe pub by the Thames, vomited on a single dose thirty-four times and evacuated twenty-two times, and 'miserably died'. But Ward discovered that she had supped on bacon and greens, a vegetable forbidden on the label. The barmaid at the Charing Cross Bagnio, who died swiftly after one drop, was similarly excusable through 'hard drinking and irregular way of living.'

Ward took the credit for the country's falling death rate. His medicine was powerfully advertised in the newspapers as a universal cure-all, and provided free for the poor (if the poor came with a churchwarden's certificate and in the afternoons) at his private hospital in Pimlico, which was graciously staffed by ladies of fashion. The *Grub Street Journal* was commendably harrying Ward, but the undying propensity of humans to swallow useless cures, from desperation or from delusion, permitted him to run four lavish London households, leave a fortune and direct himself to be buried as near the altar in Westminster Abbey as possible.

Pope was as ungrateful a patient of quacks as of doctors. His work contains scattered references to Ward, all unflattering.

> As thick as bees o'er vernal blossoms fly,
> As thick as eggs at Ward in Pillory.

> He serv'd a 'Prenticeship, who sets up shop;
> Ward try'd on Puppies, and the Poor, his Drop.
> Ev'n Radclff's Doctors travel first to France,
> Nor dare to practice till they've learn'd to dance.

> Ye shall . . .
> Not sail, with Ward, to Ape-and-monkey climes,
> Where vile Mundungus trucks for viler rhymes;

(Mundungus was stinking tobacco.)

> Safe, where no critics damn, no duns molest,
> Where wretched Withers, Ward, and Gildon rest;

(George Withers 'abused the greatest personages in power, which brought upon him frequent correction. The Marshalsea and Newgate were no strangers to him.' Charles Gildon was a Jesuit turned blasphemer.)

> Who shall decide, when Doctors disagree . . .
> Like Doctors thus, when much dispute has passed,

We find our tenets just the same at last.
Both fairly owning, Riches in effect
No grace of Heav'n or token of th' Elect;
Giv'n to the Fool, the Mad, the Vain, the Evil,
To Ward, to Waters, Chartres, and the devil.

(Francis Chartres was drummed out of the army, a cheat, usurer, swindler, pimp and rapist, who was imprisoned in Newgate, and when he died in Scotland in 1731 the populace hurled dead dogs into his grave. Waters was still alive, but risked the dead dogs.)

The shops shut up in ev'ry street,
And Fun'rals black'ning all the Doors,
And yet more melancholy Whores:
And what a dust in every place!
And a thin Court that wants your Face,
And Fevers raging up and down,
And Ward and Henley both in town!

(August in London. 'Orator Henley' dispensed universal knowledge weekly to large crowds in Lincoln's Inn Fields, and gave sermons on primitive Christianity on Sundays, and had already been noticed in the Dunciad.)

Rack'd with Sciatics, martyr'd with the Stone,
Will any mortal let himsef alone?
See Ward by batter'd Beaus invited over,
And desp'rate Misery lays hold on Dover.
The case is easier in the Mind's disease;
There all Men may be cured, whene'er they please.

Ward appears in Hogarth's 'Company of Undertakers' of 1736, on the left shoulder of the fat, cross-eyed bonesetter 'Crazy Sally' Mapp, above a dozen jostling well-wigged heads of quacks sniffing their gold-headed canes and finger-tasting their patients' urine. To have incurred the satirical genius of both Pope and Hogarth is an achievement comparable to earning a national monument.

In April 1744, Pope was dying of 'asthmatical dropsy', heart-failure with oedema of the legs. He rejected Ward for another fashionable quack, Thompson, who incised his swollen legs, drew off 'a great quantity of pure water' and assured the patient that he felt much better. Pope was tiring of 'The Doctor's Wormwood style'. 'Here am I dying from a hundred good symptoms,' he commented grumpily, before he did, aged fifty-six, shortly after his bed-ridden mother.

> *Shut, shut the door, good John! fatigu'd I said,*
> *Tye up up the knocker, say I'm sick, I'm dead.*

How many mornings have we felt like that?

$\mathcal{L}$ORD $\mathcal{B}$YRON

1728–1824

THE SHALLOWEST SCHOLAR of English literature knows that Byron had a club foot.

But which one?

His mother said the right. The constructor of his surgical appliances said the left. Fashionable author Edward Trelawny, who fought with Byron for Greek independence (he also swam the Niagara Falls), peeped at his dead friend's legs beneath his shroud and said both. Byron's publishers said the right, and they had his boots to prove it, the right sole raised half an inch on the outside. A hundred years after Byron's death, Dr H. C. Cameron inspected Byron's boots and his cobblers' lasts and said neither.

Dr Cameron diagnosed in the *Lancet* that Byron's leg muscles were wasted; and Edward Trelawny having noticed, with his postmortem glance, that both his Achilles' tendons were contracted, the cause of Byron's lameness lay in his brain. Byron suffered from Little's disease, a spacticity of the legs from cerebral damage incurred before or during birth.

The disability provoked in Byron both sensitivity and defiance. He walked by sliding along on the balls of his feet, and his mother called him a lame brat. She took him aged ten to Lavender, a Nottingham truss-maker, a quack who tried twisting the foot into shape with a wooden vice, which was ineffective but excruciating.

Byron came of a disgraceful family. His father was profligate 'Mad Jack' Byron, ex-Captain in the Guards, nephew and heir to 'Wicked' Lord Byron, who killed his cousin in a duel and dissipated the family fortune. Byron's mother was Mad Jack's second wife, a hysterical Scots heiress whose fortune her husband squandered; she went into lodgings in Aberdeen, where her son was three when his father died, pursued by his creditors to France. At ten, Byron succeeded to the Barony and the family seat of Newstead Abbey, Nottinghamshire: 'It was a change from a shabby Scotch flat to a palace.'

At Cambridge, Byron got into the bad habits of low company and high living. Flailed by debts, married only for a year (his wife accused him of insanity), nettled by the passionate attentions of Lady Caroline Lamb, he sold his library and then his ancestral home, fathered a child in Venice, appropriated from her husband the Countess Guiccioli in Ravenna, and committed incest with his half-sister Augusta in London. (It was sneaked by Harriet Beecher Stowe, author of *Uncle Tom's Cabin*, in *Macmillan's Magazine* in 1869.)

Byron was an enthusiast for the theatre and theatrical suppers, a member of the Cocoa Tree, Waiter's and the best clubs; he spoke thrice in the House of Lords, illuminated the greet Whig houses, and when wintering in Greece in 1810 swam the Hellespont. But his marital separation in 1816 was vituperative. He became vilified in the newspapers and ostracised by society, he exiled himself to Italy, and rocketed the sales of his poetry by becoming a romantic martyr. Also, he wore curl-papers in bed.

To any Englishman there was good in the man. He played cricket.

In 1805, Byron captained the Harrow XI in their initial match against Eton at Lord's—the cathedral of cricket where the poet's scorecard lies enshrined.The ground then occupied Thomas Lord's original site off the Mary-le-Bone Road, convenient for the York- shire Stingo pub, beyond it pastures rolling away northwards with grazing sheep. Byron batted at No. 9, and scored two runs. Eton thrashed them.

Byron anticipated by a century the global phobia of fat. 'I specially dread, in this world, two things, to which I believe I am equally disposed—growing fat and growing mad,' he told his ultimate doctor, Julius Millingen. 'And it would be difficult for me to decide, were I forced to make a choice, which of these conditions I should choose.'

Byron lived the slimmer's life. He rose at half past ten, drank a basin of strong green tea, rode until one then ate his meal of the day: soup, vegetables, English cheese, fried crusts, fruit, meat only once a month—even roast capon, which he loved. He reinforced his abstinence with powerful aperients, scammony, colocynth and gamboge.

Bertie Wooster mentioned later on that: 'It was my Uncle George who discovered that alcohol was a food well in advance of modern medical thought.' But Byron's doctors, too, deemed alcohol vital nourishment, and despite his scepticism towards science their patient fully agreed. He gobbled his food while downing Rhine wines and spirits, and settling down with a good book in the evening swallowed a mouthful of Holland gin per page, until at three in the morning he was pacing up and down, composing Don Juan.

Dr Millingen met Byron in November 1823 at Cephalonia, then part of the British Empire, in the Ionian Islands off the western shores of Greece. Byron had sailed from Leghorn that August in his yacht *Hercules*, a 120-ton converted collier. He had been living in Genoa when he found himself elected to the Greek Committee in London, formed by important Liberals to free Greece from the Turkish yoke, and he decided to oversee the revolution himself. The Committee had appointed the newly qualified Millingen to the Greek forces, whose care of the sick and wounded foreshadowed the Crimea. Casualties were pouring into Mesolongi, forty miles away on the mainland on the Gulf of Corinth, where on Millingen's arrival the free provision of a doctor was acclaimed by the Greeks, but his demand for a makeshift hospital was not.

After many protestations of utter poverty, unequalled by those of the most eloquent mendicant, they declared themselves unable to complete the charitable work. It certainly required no small share of barefacedness to make such assertions when so many of them wore rich dress and glittering arms; with gold coins adorning the tresses of their wives and linked doubloons forming a triangular breastplate any one of which would suffice to defray the owner's share of his sick contribution for years to come.

Byron had already lent the Greek government 20,000 Spanish dollars, and was unsurprised by Millingen's discovery. He arrived himself in Mesolongi on 6 January 1824, to a royal reception and the provision of a personal escort of guardsmen. He raised a local regiment, which he disbanded in February through its mutinous tendencies. He had Millingen made Surgeon-in-Chief of the Greek Army, at £2 a month, paid several months in arrears. Millingen wisely opened a private practice in Mesolongi, a diversion from liberating the nation which became agreeably profitable.

Millingen was now comfortably friendly with Byron, to the jealousy of the poet's personal attendant, Dr Bruno, whom he had brought from Genoa along with his faitnful valet Fletcher. One rousing evening round the punchbowl, Byron fell to the floor in an epileptic fit, foaming at the mouth, gnashing his teeth, rolling his eyes and flailing his limbs. Dr Bruno suggested venesection. The anti-scientific patient opposed this widespread surgical procedure as a fashionable fad (rightly), but settled for leeches on his temples. He continued to suffer flashes before the eyes, palpitations, faintness and indigestion. Millingen helpfully suggested giving up the drink. The thirty-six-year-old poet countered wearily:

Do you suppose I wish for life? I have grown heartily sick of it, and shall welcome the hour I shall depart from it. Why should I have regrets? Can life afford me any pleasure? Have I not enjoyed it to a surfeit? I am, literally speaking, a young old man. I have travelled, satisfied my curiosity, lost every illusion; I have exhausted all the nectar of the cup of life; it is time to throw the dregs away. Only the apprehension of two things now haunt my mind. I picture myself slowly expiring on a bed of torture, or terminating my days like Swift—a grinning idiot! Would to heaven the day were arrived in which, rushing sword in hand on a body of Turks, I might meet immediate death, the object of my wishes.

On 9 April, Byron developed fever and sore throat, with rigors and headache. Dr Bruno diagnosed rheumatic fever and venturesomely suggested bleeding. Byron objected angrily, cuttingly quoting Dr Reid's *Essays on Insanity* of 1816: less slaughter had been effected by the warrior's lance than the physician's lances. Dr Millingen protested that meant only nervous, not feverish, cases. Byron rounded:

Who is nervous if I am not? Do not these words, besides, apply to my case? Drawing blood from a nervous person is like loosening the chords of a musical instrument, the tones of which are already defective for want of sufficient tension.

Millingen lost patience with this poetic procrastination:

Chagrined at this, I laid aside all consideration for his feelings, and solemnly assured him how deeply I lamented to see him trifle with his life in this manner. I told him that his pertinacious refusal to be bled had caused a precious opportunity to be lost; that a few hours of hope still remained; but that unless he would submit immediately to be bled, neither Dr Bruno nor myself could answer for the consequences.

He added to this deadly ultimatum that the disease, if not killing him, might send him mad. The argument worked.

Casting at us both the fiercest glance of vexation, he threw out his arm and said in the most angry tone: 'Come; you are, I see, a damned set of butchers. Take away as much blood as you will; but have done with it.'

They took twenty ounces. The fever rose, the sufferer became delirious. Next day, they bled him twice, taking two pounds of blood until the patient stopped them. They applied cold poultices to his head and raised blisters on his body (above the knees: Byron objected to their seeing his deformed foot). Millingen enlisted two local doctors as reinforcements, but Byron stipulated that the consultation should be conducted in silence: they took his pulse, eyed his tongue, looked him up and down, shook their heads and left.

The established doctors grew alarmed. Their patient seemed to have inflammation of the brain. They put leeches behind his ears, raised a huge blister between his shoulders and applied mustard-plasters, now unimpeded, to his feet. They forcefully dosed him with stinking valerian, ingredient of smelling-salts. The patient became comatose and died at 6 o'clock on the evening of Easter Monday, 19 April.

The post-mortem showed encephalitis, enlargement of the heart and sclerosis of the liver: the feet were overlooked. Byron probably died from malaria. The heart and brains were sealed in a chest and embarked ceremoniously for the nearby island of Zante, to a twenty-five gun salute, one burst for each year of the poet's thirty-seven. The rest of the body was put in another chest and sent home to Nottingham. Lady Caroline Lamb unexpectedly ran into the funeral procession, never recovered from the shock and died four years later.

Unlike Rupert Brooke at Skiros in the Aegean Sea, Byron left no corner of a foreign field that is for ever England. Rupert Brooke, too, was prepared to die sword in hand and did so of a fever; but his poetry is Grantchester's chime against Byron's boom like the bells of St Paul's.

Dr Millingen ended up with a splendid job in Egypt, doctor to Ibrahim Pasha's harem.

$\mathcal{P}$ERCY $\mathcal{B}$YSSHE $\mathcal{S}$HELLEY

1729–1822

*I*T IS PLEASANT for any writer to discover an affinity with Shelley.

In the spring of 1811, Shelley became, like myself, a medical student at St Bartholomew's Hospital, which was founded by the monk Rahere in 1123 and refounded by King Henry VIII in 1544. Its graceful blocks of Bath stone wards, lying between the soaring spiritual inspiration of St Paul's Cathedral and the earthy butchery of Smithfield Meat Market, frame a spacious tree-shaded square with a lavish fountain and an ornate gateway depicting its founder King. Hogarth's only mural, *The Pool of Bethesda*, decorates the staircase leading to its Great Hall. 'Bart's' comprises in itself the parish of St Bartholomew-the-Less. The Great Fire of 1666 smoked itself out in Cock Lane against its walls; the blitz left its wanton craters; it is the pantheon of William Harvey, Percival Pott and James Paget; it has succoured the ills and mishaps of the City of London for 875 years, and is now eyed by the British National Health Service as a redundant antiquity.

Shelley had signed up for the anatomy lectures of John Aberne-thy, a surgeon of dramatic phraseology: 'Live on sixpence a day and earn it', he advised fat City men, directing their fat wives to buy skipping-ropes. Difficult patients he referred for a second opinion to Dr Robertson of Inverness, whom they discovered not to exist when they got there. The lectures were paid for by the students, and pirated by the *Lancet*, to Mr Abernethy's fury.

The Shelleys had a medical tradition. The father of Percy Shelley's grandfather, who was the Baronet Sir Bysshe, was an American quack doctor from Newark, New Jersey. Sir Bysshe himself in the 1780s profited from the fat flock of the superquack

James Graham, the former Edinburgh medical student whose magnetised and musical Grand Celestial Bed, installed in his cure-all Temple of Health in Pall Mall, ecstatically overcame infertility at £100 a night (including breakfast). Shelley's cousin Charles Grove was a medical student, to whose sister Harriet young Shelley became engaged on leaving Eton: but she broke it off, leaving him with giddy attacks.

Shelley was briefly at Bart's. His mind was like a skylark, ever winging and singing and soaring off somewhere else. Four years afterwards, across the Thames at Guy's Hospital, John Keats became a conscientious medical student who qualified with credit as a Licenciate of the Society of Apothecaries in July 1816.

Shelley was lodging at 15 Poland Street in Soho, having been sent down from Oxford. When he had returned after Christmas for his first Hilary Term at University College, he wrote under the pseudonym 'Jeremiah Stukeley' *The Necessity of Atheism*. This was a pamphlet at sixpence, displayed in the window of Munday & Slatter, booksellers in the High. It was a geometrical theorem that disproved the existence of God, as Pythagoras had proved that the square on the hypotenuse equalled the square on the other two sides.

It started:

A close examination of the validity of the proofs adduced to support any proposition, has ever been allowed to be the only sure way of attaining truth, upon the advantages of which it is unnecessary to descant.

And ended:

QED.

The eighteen-year-old undergraduate was right. A moment's thought acknowledges that there is no more proof of the existence of God than of the existence of finite time and space beyond our cosy universe. God in His Heaven is a product of human imagination, stimulated by vanity and fright. Why should we human animals enjoy a life everlasting, denied to our dogs and cats? The unpopularity of death, exploited by the gathering of corpses round churches and the monopoly of funerals, has empowered intelligent but bossy men to invent our souls, and to take charge of them for us. As suchlike persons ran Oxford, Shelley was instantly in trouble; though to invite wider discussion of his arguments he had sent copies of *The Necessity of Atheism* to the Chancellor of Oxford University, the heads and deans on every Oxford college, and to the entire bench of bishops, with the compliments of Jeremiah Stukeley. He was given overnight to quit his rooms.

Shelley started skylarking with women. He was a man of such fickle mind, of such unstable personality, that at Eton it had necessitated the Physician to the Royal Household at Windsor to prevent his father installing him in an asylum. A fellow pupil of his two sisters, at Mrs Fening's Academy for Young Ladies in Clapham Common, was coffee-house keeper's daughter sixteen-year-old Harriet Westbrook. Shelley eloped with her to Scotland, where they married in Edinburgh on 28 August 1811. The first night of their honeymoon at a local tavern was interrupted by customers offering to perform the ancient Scottish ritual of washing the bride in whisky. They went to live at Tan-yr-allt near Rhyl in north Wales, where in the night of 26 February 1813 Evan the shepherd fired three pistol-shots at Shelley for worrying his sheep.

That year, they had a daughter. The next, they separated. Harriet went to Bath, four months pregnant, a boy was born at eight months which Shelley doubted was his. On 10 December 1816 Harriet was washed up drowned in the Serpentine in Hyde Park, as Harriet Smith of Hans Place in Knightsbridge, advanced in pregnancy by someone unknown. She had been missing for six weeks. 'She had a valuable ring on her finger,' recorded *The Times*. 'A want of honour in her own conduct is supposed to have led to this fatal catastrophe, her husband being abroad.' Shelley had been in Switzerland, on the shores of Lake Geneva, living across a vineyard from Byron.

A fortnight later, Shelley married at St Mildred's, Bread Street, in the City, nineteen-year-old Mary Wollstonecraft Godwin, author of *Frankenstein*, with whom he already had a year-old son. The Lord

Chancellor denied him custody of dead Harriet's children, on the grounds that he was likely to inspire them with his own condemnable principles of conduct: Shelley passed them to Dr Hume, a worthy army doctor, at £120 a year. The newly wed couple went to live at Marlow, beside the Thames.

Shelley's skylark mind winged round his health. He became a vegetarian:

> There is no disease, bodily or mental, which adoption of vegetable diet and pure water has not infallibly mitigated.

And a hypochondriac. He decided that he had contracted elephantiasis.

Elephantiasis is a tropical disease, which was established in 1877 to be caused by the filarial worm *Wuchereria bancrofti*, transmitted by the bite of infected mosquitoes. The worm can grow three inches long and block the channels of the clear body-fluid, lymph. But noninfective elephantiasis can occur anywhere in the world, from congenital, or chronic, blockage of the lymph ducts. The lymph dams up, causing enormous swelling of the arms or legs, or of the scrotum, which has been recorded as necessitating a wheelbarrow for the patient's locomotion.

Robert Liston, the Scottish surgeon who performed the First European operation under anaesthesia in 1846, had been expelled after a row with his colleagues from the Edinburgh Royal Infirmary. In defiance, he operated spectacularly all over Edinburgh, and removed an elephantiasis scrotum weighing forty-four and a half pounds. The possibility of such an encumbrance terrified the handsome, trim, lanky Shelley. He became convinced that he had contracted elephantiasis from a fat-legged old woman in a crowded stage-coach. A surgeon was consulted, who said of course he hadn't. The patient was unconvinced. He would suddenly roll on the floor, twisting like an eel, excusing himself to onlookers: 'I have the elephantiasis!' His friend the novelist Thomas Love Peacock recorded:

He used to draw the skin of his own hand, arms and neck very tight, and if he discovered any deviation, he would seize the person next to him and endeavour by a corresponding pressure to see if any corresponding deviation existed.

Even today, this abrupt behaviour would arouse suspicions in adjacent young women.

In 1813, Shelley suffered pains in the chest, announced that he was going to die, and like many of the contemporary literati took to laudanum. When Peacock called:

He caught up with a bottle of laudanum, and said, 'I never part from this'. Then he quoted Sophocles, 'Man's happiest lot is not to be . . .'

He coughed blood, and specified that he was rapidly going to die from phthisis. In 1815, Dr Christopher Pemberton, the King's Physician-Extraordinary, agreed with him and pronounced sentence of approaching death. Shelley instantly became much better. That September, he went for a trip up the Thames:

The exercise and dissipation of mind attached to such an expedition have produced a favourable effect on my health, that my habitual dejection and irritability have almost deserted me.

A friend on the jaunt was delighted:

In Shelley the change is quite remarkable; he has now the ruddy, healthy complexion of the autumn upon his countenance, and he is twice as fat as he used to be.

Peacock ascribed this improvement to his abandoning vegetarianism and taking to well peppered mutton chops. But Shelley's ills returned. On 26 October 1816 he began obsessively to weigh the food he ate daily (that day, it was twenty-two ounces).

Shelley returned to Bart's, to consult Sir William Lawrence. Sir William was the lecturer in surgery who succeeded Abernethy, and who shared his technique for distancing difficult patients. He advised Shelley to live abroad. On 12 March 1818 Shelley went to Italy, a country with a climate so agreeably mild that, whenever winter came, you felt that spring could not be far behind.

In September, he made himself sick from overeating Italian cakes. In November, he was diagnosed in Naples as suffering from liver disease, and as a cure was prescribed riding. In 1820, the Professor of Surgery at Pisa diagnosed renal disease. Shelley panicked that he might be cut for stone, and rapidly recovered. The Pisa Professor succeeded in putting him off laudanum, for which Shelley substituted the commendably non-toxic hypnotism, relaxing in his easily induced trances.

His letters were full of his ills.

You will find me a wretched invalid unless a great change should take place,

he wrote on 16 April 1820. He added more cheerfully on 1 May:

I have been seriously ill since I last wrote to you, but I am now recovering.

In August he wrote to Robert Southey:

I have had sickness enough, and at this moment I have so severe a pain in my side that I can hardly write.

How he echoed Pope! 'This long disease, my life.'
'Through life he was a martyr to pain and debility,' recorded his second wife. But his friend Edward Trelawny said:

I often saw him in a state of nudity, and he always reminded me of a young Indian, strong-limbed, and vigorous, and barring drugs and accidents, he might have lived as long as his father— to be ninety.

Shelley attempted suicide in London and in Naples, recovering both times by his doctor insisting that he keep walking round the room. He wrote to Edward Trelawny in the summer of 1822 saying he would like to keep some deadly prussic acid about him, just in case.

Shelley enjoyed skylarking in boats. Though he was not a born seaman:

Shelley was awkward as a woman in all things appertaining to boats, but full of good intentions. He tangled himself up in the rigging, read Sophocles while trying to steer and several times just missed falling overboard.

His *Ariel* was built on a naval officer's design for his friend and fellow yachting enthusiast Ellerker Williams, a twenty-nine-year old former East India Company cavalry officer. *Ariel* had delightful lines, but needed two tons of iron ballast to stabilise her. Shelley originally named her *Don Juan*, but after a row with Byron he was obliged to change it. The name was painted across her mainsail, resistant to soap and deck scrubbing-brushes, and to turpentine: they had to slice the canvas.

A week after his suicidal hint to Trelawny, Shelley, Williams and a young crewman Charles Vivian, sailed from Leghorn northwards to Lerici in *Ariel* and were lost in a squall without trace. Their bodies were washed ashore over the next four weeks, Shelley first, all eaten by marine life. They were temporarily buried in the sands, then dug up by a squad of Tuscan soldiers with mattocks and tongs, Williams reappearing in detachable bits. Shelley was already half-consumed by a covering of lime, but was burnt on the seashore in ancient Greek fashion, soaked by oil and incense; for its ignition, 'more wine was poured over Shelley's dead body than he had ever consumed during life.' The brains bubbled in the skull. The cremation was performed in the presence of Byron and the village children, who whispered to each other that the gathered bones and the ashes, once they were home in England, would come again to life.

Apart from an attack of conjunctivitis at Marlow in December 1817, Shelley never had a day's illness in his brief life.

Thomas Carlyle

1795–1881

At nine o'clock on a lovely London summer's morning in 1843, you sit at your desk downstairs at No. 5 Cheyne Row in arty Chelsea, shoot your cuffs, dip your Perry's Birmingham steel-nibbed pen into your pewter ink-well, and start on the first sheet of your pile of lined foolscap paper:

Oliver Cromwell's Letters and Speeches

Chapter 1

Anti-Dryasdust

You pause in thought, and continue:

> What and how great are the interests which connect themselves with the hope that England may yet attain to some practical belief and understanding of its History during the Seventeenth Century, need not be insisted on at present; such hope being still very distant, very uncertain . . .

> *'Damn and blast her eyeballs!'*

You hurl your pen to the Turkey carpet, spattering it with blue-black ink, leap up and glare through the open window. That bloody young woman next door has started practising the piano again.

Carlyle could only slam the window, and concentrate upon

Oliver Cromwell with an intensity that—unavailingly—sought deafness against the ever-repeated tinkles of *Für Eliza*.

Twenty years pass. Carlyle writes:

> Meanwhile, all I had to say of him is finished: that too, it seems, was a bit of work appointed to be done. Adieu, good readers; bad also, adieu.

Drawing a line underneath with his ebony ruler, he replaces his pen, folds his arms and contemplates the end of *The History of Frederick the Great* (ten volumes) in restful silence.

He had built across the roof at Cheyne Row a soundproof room of unperforated outer and inner walls, lit by skylights, impervious to all noise but the perching birds, cost £170. For a man enjoying the superb self-confidence of overwhelming egotism, waiting until his books tickled the public intellect profitably enough had been frustrating. The piano-player was by then married and spawning a rowdy family.

Carlyle was sensitive to noise as a Capitol goose in Ancient Rome. It was the least torturing of the neuroses which kicked and wriggled inside him like unborn devils.

Thomas Carlyle's prose enjoys the grandeur of Victorian architecture. His books are useful and assertive monuments of their age, like the Albert Hall and the steam-lofted spires of St Pancras Station. His idiosyncratic style he could apply impartially to describing events occurring in the French Revolution and in his own body.

Carlyle's Sufferings

(1) *Indigestion*. 'It is as if a rat was gnawing at my stomach . . . The accursed hag, dyspepsia, had got me bitted and bridled, and was ever striving to make my waking, living day a thing of ghastly nightmares. I resisted what I could; never did yield or surrender to her. One could not call it hope, but only desperate obstinacy that animated me—obstinacy as of ten mules.'

(2) *Constipation*. 'Rebellion of the intestines . . . stools of pipe-

clay state.' He became 'dull, stupid and unable to work' unless he enjoyed hefty bowel movements, to be grudgingly executed by Epsom salts, mercury powder and castor-oil: 'Unless I dose myself with that oil of sorrow I cannot get along at all.'

(3) *Insomnia.* 'Three weeks without any kind of sleep, from impossibility to be free from noise . . . sick with sleeplessness, nervous, bilious, splenetic . . . I fight with dullness and bile in the forenoons as of old . . . my nerves, my nerves.'

(4) *Miscellaneous symptoms.* Mind shot with black streaked lightning. Sensation of fire rushing through body. Desiccation: 'I was wasted and fretted to a thread. My tongue, let me drink as I would, continued as dry as charcoal.'

Carlyle's Treatment

(1) An unnamed medical 'long hairy-eared jackass' stopped him smoking.

(2) 'Stomach Cure' Bedams was a patent medicine man in Birmingham, with whom Carlyle stayed for two months of dieting and exercises. 'I have been bephysicked and bedrugged, I have swallowed about two stouppels of castor oil since I came hither.' In vain.

(3) A sympathizer gave him a horse when he was forty-four; he rode until he was seventy-four, when he fell off. Horses had no effect on his symptoms.

(4) Walking, sea-bathing off the White Cliffs of Dover, country food, changing his dinner-hour, were all of no avail He took the Malvern waters under Dr Gully, the famed hydrotherapist who became more famous when his mistress was poisoned by her husband, the barrister Charles Bravo, who then killed himself.

(5) Queen Victoria's physician Sir Richard Quain diagnosed: 'The wretched dyspepsia to which he was subject was fully accounted for by the fact that he was particularly fond of a very nasty gingerbread.'

(6) Carlyle's elder brother was a doctor, but they wisely avoided each other.

Carlyle's Sex Life

Carlyle's impotence was the sneer of London literati, the chuckle of London clubs. In 1826 in Dumfriesshire, where he was born, he married vivacious, snappish Jenny, a doctor's daughter aged twenty-five, related across 300 years to the monstrously politically incorrect John Knox. Like her husband, she suffered agonisingly from sleeplessness and noise, she took opium (which was then unremarkable) and smoked cigarettes (which was shocking).

They honeymooned at home at Comely Bank, Edinburgh. The bride went to bed alone, reflecting that her new hubby had not kissed her all day. This oversight was compounded by his joining her in bed and masturbating. Such therapy proved as ineffective as that applied to his stomach. Jenny at first desired to kiss and caress him, but as the self-treatment silently continued she felt indignant, then tickled by the absurdity of her shattered first night and burst out laughing. Carlyle muttered scornfully 'Woman!', then left her bed for one in the next room. The next morning, he tore up the herbaceous border outside in fury.

He never went to bed with her again. Once facing the prospect after dining out in the London suburbs, where there was only one bed for the two of them, he rode home to Chelsea at 11 p.m. rather than share it. 'The body part seemed so little to me, I had no idea it could mean much to her,' Carlyle confessed later— admittedly to Frank Harris, author of the five-volume *My Life and Loves* and a verbose sexual Munchausen.

James Anthony Froude, author of the *History of England from the Fall of Wolsey to the Spanish Armada* in twelve volumes, was Carlyle's literary executor. He grasped before its time the cash value of a swift biography with all the sexy bits. Froude got his 'weird and uncanny' secrets from the unnoticeable novelist Geraldine Jewsbury, Jenny's 'confidential friend', who had confessed to her 'vague undefined yearnings to be yours in some way'.

Froude's *My Relations with Carlyle*, published after his own death in 1903, reflated the impotence story. It provoked Carlyle's fellow Dumfriessian Sir James Crichton-Browne, physician, hero-worshipper of the literary expert on Hero-Worship, and the Queen's Visitor in Lunacy, to a thunderstorm of outraged pomposity flashing from eight columns of the *British Medical Journal*.

> Who would believe that this man of noble soul, of unimpeachable honour, would blight a young woman's life by drawing her into a marriage that was no marriage. No! No! that would not do, and besides any allegation of that kind might have been steadily refuted. There were those who had seen Carlyle bathing.

Frank Harris described graphically how the gingerbread man Sir Richard Quain had confided over dinner at the Garrick Club in London his examination of Mrs Carlyle in her bedroom. Sir Richard tossed her skirts over her head, pulled her legs apart, dragged her to the edge of the bed, inserted his speculum into her vulva, then sprang up with the cry: 'Why you're a virgo intacta!' According to Froude, this condition was confirmed post-mortem by the house surgeon at St George's Hospital, where poor Jenny was taken after a fatal heart attack riding in her new brougham in nearby Hyde Park. 'It is almost superfluous to identify it as the coinage of Ananias and Sapphira,' Sir James dismissed the story—though to make sure, quoted gynaecologists who had discovered that contraction of the vulva can anyway occur naturally after the menopause.

Jenny was as neurotic as Thomas. She suffered from dyspepsia, vertigo, paralysis, depression and paranoia, occasioning him to say things like: 'My dear, I think I never saw you looking more bilious; your face is *green* and your eyes all *bloodshot*.' Occasionally, he mildly battered her. But he loved her homemade marmalade, 'pure as liquid amber.'

Diagnosis

Carlyle's dyspepsia, impotence, hypochondria, insomnia and other oddities are symptoms of an anxiety neurosis and depression.

As psychiatry had not been invented, this was difficult to cure. 'Of all the sons of Adam, men of medicine are the most unprofitable,' Carlyle had the effrontery to conclude before dropping dead aged eighty-five.

ELIZABETH BARRETT BROWNING

1806–1861

ELIZABETH BARRETT was a difficult young woman.

Like Napoleon's Josephine and Nelson's Fanny, she originated amid the sugar and slaves, the rum and riches, of the West Indies.

Marie Rose (who was Josephine—Napoleon changed his women's names to taste) was born in volcanic Martinique in the Windward Islands in 1763. In 1779, she married the local Vicomte de Beauharnais, an enthusiast for both the American and French Revolutions, who was unsportingly guillotined in Paris in 1794. When Josephine met Napoleon the following year, Martinique had been captured by the Royal Navy, and she was penniless.

On equally volcanic Nevis in the Leewards, in March 1787, Captain Horatio Nelson of the twenty-eight gun frigate *Boreas* married the President's niece, a doctor's widow with a son, the bride being given away by post-Captain Prince William, to be Britain's sailor King.

Elizabeth Barrett's grandfather was Charles Moulton, a rascal from Madeira, who enjoyed four families and plentiful mistresses. He married into the family in Jamaica in 1781. His son Edward adopted the Barrett name and migrated to England, married and had twelve children. The price of sugar and slaves had dropped disastrously by 1809, but Edward Barrett could afford £27,000 to buy 500 acres of the Malvern Hills in Herefordshire, including the country house Hope End, which he immediately rebuilt to resemble the Prince Regent's oriental Pavilion at Brighton.

Elizabeth Barrett, fittingly born in another country house in Durham, moved in aged three. She was a dreadful child: selfish, stubborn, sulky, pushy and precocious, bad-temperedly bossing about her younger brothers and sisters, always knocking over the furniture and throwing around the books. She grew into a five-foot tall young woman, with—according to her friend Mary Russell Mitford, author of the 1819 rural life hit *Our Village*:

> a slight, delicate figure, with a shower of dark curls falling on each side of a most expressive face; large, tender eyes, richly fringed by dark eye-lashes, and a smile like a sunbeam.

She wrote her first poem aged six, on virtue, which got from her father 10 shillings. Elizabeth matured under five black clouds.

1. *The Electra complex.*

    At twelve, she was writing about a father 'whose unwearied affection I can never repay'. At puberty, she had developed father-fixation. She saw him as a benevolent man of power—he was High Sheriff of Herefordshire—and backed him in his rows with mother. She was terrified of thunderstorms, and felt that Edward Barrett contained their unexploded magnificent violence. Her greatest pleasure was to afford him pleasure; his tearful distress at her frequent illnesses was her constant delight. In her thirties, he would bring flowers home for her from work, his footstep on the stairs a vibrant thrill. A door joined the bedrooms of father and daughter, and at midnight he would come to chat and to pray, holding hands, alone. He kissed her good night and left her in a repose approaching postcoital profundity.

2. *Anxiety, agoraphobia, anorexia.*

    Elizabeth was frightened of the dark, and of its bats. She had attacks of raging headache and of helpless weakness. She frightened everyone with hyperventilation—an over-breathing which blew the carbon dioxide from her blood, constricted her cerebral and cardiac arteries to produce alarming pains, and was relieved only when her breathing stopped, to await rekindling by her mounting CO_2.

    In her teens, she developed agoraphobia—fear of going

into the open or venturing far from home—and she refused to move from her room at Hope End (a useful symptom in so industrious a writer). Next, she had anorexia nervosa, which is not a simple loss of desire to eat, but a deliberate refusal, the food often being hidden, or secretly vomited. Sufferers develop a voracious appetite (the 'canine hunger'), gorge themselves, feel guilty and induce vomiting, straying into the matching complaint of bulimia nervosa.

Elizabeth lived on slops or dry toast, except if she fancied something hotly devilled or curried. Her alarming emaciation, her helpless flopping in bed, had the family fussing round her desperately. She unemotionally presented to her illness and to its sympathetic carnival *la belle indifférence*, described by imaginative Professor Charcot in Paris fifty years later. Anorexia nervosa, too, had to wait fifty years before it was identified by Queen Victoria's sharp physician Sir William Gull.

As the treatment of all affluent, but regrettably undiagnosed, patients throughout Europe was taking the waters, Elizabeth's hopeful doctors booked her for a year into the handy Spa Hotel at Gloucester.

The causes of these three conditions were the mingling shadows in a neurotic personality, which reacted abnormally, or excessively, to the everyday problems of life. Each one of them expressed the subconscious mind's control of the body, and the hysterical dissociation of the personality from the disease. Elizabeth concentrated the world upon herself, like the sun viewed in its partial eclipse. Her weakness was her strength. She controlled her family, she retained childhood dependence upon her parents, while the competition of her growing siblings was sidelined. She need not face the sexual awkwardness of adult life. She need not be woman, but could remain delightfully daddy's girl.

Though everybody in Herefordshire knew that her troubles resulted from hurting her back while unskillfully saddling her pony one morning in 1824.

3. *Opium addiction*.

Elizabeth nightly fell asleep 'in a red hood of poppies.' She started on opium in her teens, and in Torquay was hitting 1,000 drops of laudanum a day (laudanum was the popular tincture of opium, dissolved in 90 per cent alcohol). Her daily intake would have filled 100 old-fashioned teaspoons, enough to dose a ward of forty hospital patients. The Opium King De Quincey was at the time on 8,000 drops a day, but was trying to cut it down.

Such extravagant dosages were necessitated by the swiftly mounting tolerance to laudanum's active ingredient, morphine. Elizabeth was swallowing over ten times the safe dose. She took her laudanum with ether, or added a few tots of brandy, or some reasonable port. Her addiction absorbed her entire income of £200 a year: she genteelly excused it by comparing her dose to Southey's 'Amreeta-cup of immortality'.

Nobody bothered much about opium addicts, who were regarded as oddities, like balloonists. Coleridge took laudanum all his life—he said for his rheumatism—Keats, Walter Scott, Wilkie Collins and Dickens liked their drop, and Florence Nightingale implanted opium under the skin of her thigh with a silver scalpel.

The poppy flourished across mid-nineteenth century Britain. Chemist's shops were full of cheap 'cordials' and 'pick-me-ups', like 'Fire Brigade Mixture' and 'Black Drop', all potent with opium. 'Mrs Winslow's Soothing Syrup' and 'Infants' Quietness' were poured lavishly into children to induce stupor, allowing poor mothers to enjoy gainful days, and affluent ones peaceful nights. In 1868, a Poisons Act began to control such narcotic liberality: in the next century, the tobacco-leaf flourished across the land more luxuriously, and far more lethally.

Elizabeth absorbed opium until her death, and never let her father know the grip of her unbreakable habit.

4. *Tuberculosis*.

Early in 1838, Elizabeth coughed up blood and was

diagnosed by her Dr Chambers as suffering from phthisis. Keats had exclaimed in the same circumstances: 'That drop of blood is my death warrant. I must die'—to be proved right in a year. The short-lived Brontë sisters Anne, Emily and Charlotte were at the time sitting breathing fatally over each other in Haworth parsonage. Nobody knew that phthisis was an infectious disease until forty-four years later, when the microbiological impresario Robert Koch dramatically presented his latest discovery, the tubercule bacillus.

Phthisis was feared as a widespread affliction which wrought holes in the lungs, all running with pus and blood, and leading steadily to emaciation and death. Finding no cavities in Elizabeth's lungs, Dr Chambers treated her with leeches and suggested the air of Torquay. Most tuberculous patients were buoyed by *spes phthisica*, a strange and helpful hopefulness; but Elizabeth continued to flop in bed, contentedly miserable. Her father had to neglect his business in London to hold her hand in Torquay; to pray with her, and let her 'draw nearer than ever'.

In 1840, her doctors agreed she was cured. She was as lucky as Somerset Maugham a century later, who thirty years before the discovery of streptomycin recovered from TB in Switzerland, and with his usual economy of material wrote a best-seller about it, *Sanatorium*.

5. *Death of Brother*.

Elizabeth's bright brother Edward ('Bro') was born fifteen months after her. She dominated him most fondly. When Elizabeth was at the breezy Devon resort of Torquay for her cure, on 11 July 1840, Bro with a couple of friends and a crewman took a boat trip across an unruffled Tor Bay, and like Shelley off Leghorn eighteen years earlier sank unseen. It took three weeks for Bro's body to be washed up on the beach at nearby Babbacombe, consumed by marine life. Elizabeth's existence was henceforth threaded with the need of a man to provide the useful mental stimulus of Bro, and as intimately.

Elizabeth started an affair with Hugh Boyd in 1826, when she was twenty. He was a handsome Irishman, a poet *manqué*, a Greek buff, author of *Select Passages from the Greek Fathers*, who lived with his wife and daughter at Ruby Cottage near Hope End. He was forty-six and was going blind. He wrote a letter expressing his delight at her poetry and inviting her to call. Her father objected to such impropriety. After a year's chummy correspondence, Elizabeth visited Boyd weekly, and they recited Greek poetry to one another. Father had so relented as to send a brace of pheasants.

Elizabeth began arriving at seven a.m., before anyone at the cottage was up and dressed, infuriating Mrs Boyd. (As Elizabeth herself usually never rose before midday, this convincingly indicates the strength of her passion.) With father's permission, she stayed there three weeks, reciting more Greek.

> *If old Bacchus were the speaker*
> *He would tell you with a sigh,*
> *Of the Cyprus in this beaker*
> *I am sipping like a fly,—*

she started the first of twenty-two stanzas of *Wine of Cyprus*, the poem addressed to Hugh Boyd in appreciation of the *vin de table* at Ruby Cottage.

In 1833, Boyd followed Elizabeth during three earlier years which she had spent in Devon for her health, not at Torquay but at equally breezy Sidmouth; she was beginning to think him unintelligent, and to her relief he took his family off to Bath. When he died in 1848, she wrote gracefully, and gratefully:

> *Steadfast friend,*
> *Who never didst my heart or life misknow,*
> *Nor either's faults too keenly apprehend,—*

Boyd never met her father.

Elizabeth's later suitors included the evangelist minister at Sidmouth, and Hengist Home, the Mexican adventurer, Australian gold-digger and poet, but he was eccentric, giggled, poured water over himself during dinner and played the guitar.

The slaves of Jamaica were unfortunately liberated, bringing the Barretts financial embarrassment. They sold Hope End in the summer of 1832 for £50,000, and in 1837 became the Barretts of Wimpole Street (the successful play was in 1930, followed by the equally successful movie).

On Tuesday 20 May 1845, Robert Browning blew into No. 50 Wimpole Street, invited by Elizabeth between two and six. His visit was the consummation of an intense correspondence since January, his first letter starting: 'I love your verses with all my heart, my dear Miss Barrett,' and ending, 'and I love you too.' this was a thoughtful two-pronged approach to a susceptible poetess.

Elizabeth was thirty-nine, and had been recently redescribed by Mary Mitford:

She has totally lost the rich, bright colouring which certainly made the greater part of her beauty. She is dark and pallid; the hair is almost hidden; the look of youth gone.

She had taken a dislike to bright lights, and received her teatime visitors with the curtains drawn.

Robert was thirty-three, handsome, son of a Bank of England clerk from Camberwell down the Old Kent Road, his mother partly German. A bursting-out poet and playwright, he was writing his rousing *How They Brought the Good News from Ghent to Aix* (whatever it was) and his Disney prototype *The Pied Piper of Hamelin*. He incited the inflamed Elizabeth to slip out at eleven in the morning on Saturday 12 September 1846, and marry him in nearby Marylebone Church, attended only by her lady's maid.

The couple parted immediately. Elizabeth appeared at the Hampstead house of her old boyfriend Hugh Boyd, who gave her a glass of wine (probably the awful Cyprus). She wrote a note: 'Papa I am married; I hope you will not be too displeased.' He replied expelling her from his life.

A week later, Elizabeth slipped away from No. 50 while the

family was at dinner, attended only by her spaniel Flush. She joined Robert for a filthy crossing from Southampton to Le Havre, took a week in Paris, then ten days by carriage down the rain-swept Rhône, and after a trying month's travelling—journeying made Elizabeth helplessly fragile, to the point of fainting—they settled in Pisa. Here copulation first occurred, it is pleasant to think under the Freudian influence of its leading item of architecture.

Anorexia had left Elizabeth an unpractised housewife. She could cook only toast, which she burnt. They lived on takeaways, washed down by Elizabeth with Chianti by the tumblerful. In 1847 they settled in Florence, where two years later she had a son Robert (who became a sculptor), the middle pregnancy among four aborting ones.

Their home was a floor in the Palazzo Guidi, where the couple loved, rowed and were bored, like unpoetic others (a bone of contention was Robert's installing a fresh skeleton with a readily detachable skull to help with his drawing lessons). Elizabeth's daily opium was embittered with Robert's disapproval. She immersed herself in spiritualism. They took trips to London: she met Florence Nightingale early in the Crimean war, and rightly perceived her a woman far too intelligent to be a nurse. She never again saw her father.

In midsummer 1861, she developed a cough and difficulty in breathing, treated by mustard plasters and mustard foot-baths: she died suddenly, perhaps from a myocardial infarct or from a pulmonary embolus. She was buried in the Protestant cemetery in Florence. Robert died in Venice twenty-eight years later, and was buried in Westminster Abbey. In life, she was the more famous. She wrote a plenitude of somewhat wishy-washy poetry, much of it ill-rhymed. He was an equally industrious versifier, but one of genius, if often of puzzling obscurity.

Eight years after Elizabeth's death, Robert tried to marry wealthy Lady Ashburton, but was turned down. In the last summer of his life, he castigated the defunct Edward Fitzgerald, who had never known Elizabeth, but who Robert had discovered in print 'thanked God my wife was dead':

Surely to spit there glorifies your face—
Spitting from lips once sanctified by Hers.

Perhaps his love endured. Or perhaps the temptation of such a *bon mot* was irresistible.

Refreshingly among poets, Robert Browning was an unflinching optimist:

One who never turned his back but marched breastforward,
Never doubted clouds would break,
Never dreamed, though right were worsted, wrong would triumph,
Held we fall to rise, are baffled to fight better,
Sleep to wake.

His encouragement: 'Greet the unseen with a cheer!' was published on the day of his death.

But he was not entirely the man of the world. He wrote in *Pippa Passes*:

Then, owls and bats,
Cowls and twats,
Monks and nuns, in a cloister's moods,
Adjourn to the oak-stump pantry!

Dear me! Nobody had told him that a nun's twat was not part of her habit.

CHARLES DICKENS

1812–1870

SHAKESPEARE PLUNGES us into depths of the human soul like Clarence into the butt of Malmsey. Dickens tickles us as the master of human grotesqueries. Literary England despised Dickens as vulgar. He is magnificently vulgar. In the smoky, gaslit, candle-flickering parlours of his age there was nothing to do all evening except play the piano and sing. Dickens and an armchair vividly enticed the imagination. He anticipated the movies, radio and television. How sad, that the consistent excellence of his entertainment has escaped his successors.

Dickens' magically cranky characters suffer few recognisable maladies. The Fat Boy—'I wants to make your flesh creep'—who was Mr Wardle's servant Joe at Dingley Dell in *Pickwick Papers*, 'a fat and red-faced boy, in a state of somnolency', has migrated to our more literate physiology books as an example of hypothalamic dysfunction. A peculiar fellow guest at a Brighton hotel in 1849 became Mr Dick in *David Copperfield*, a case of obsessional ruminations about King Charles's head. Dickens 'kills his children as if he liked it', but they die suddenly and inexplicably.

His own infant daughter, Dora Annie, died after brief convulsions on 14 April 1851, the news whispered to him while chairing a meeting of the General Theatrical Fund in the London Tavern. He had named her after Little Dora, the heroine of *David Copperfield*: 'It was an ill-omened name', he muttered, reflecting how fiction foreshadows life. This sadness was a fortnight after Mr Macawber—his father, John Dickens—had died in his Bloomsbury flat following a bladder operation, inexplicably performed without chloroform (which had been fashionable for three years), leaving his room 'a slaughterhouse of blood'.

Dickens created unmemorable doctors (fiery Doctor Slammer of the 97th, Mr Winkle's challenger to pistols at sunset, is untroubled with medical functions). But his depiction of medical students rings with eternal truth. Benjamin Allen and Bob Sawyer, lodging at Lant Street beside the Thames, are uproariously grotesque: hearty young men tripping their carefree way among the blackest horrors of human life, as cheerfully familiar with the human body, alive or dead, as with their breakfast. Mr Pickwick thought highly of medical students: 'They are fine fellows; very fine fellows; with judgments matured by observation and reflection; tastes refined by reading and study'—but on that page he had not come to know them personally.

For such overflowing accuracy, Dickens in his twenties surely mingled with medical students—and lawyers' pupils—while he was a shorthand-writer at the ecclesiastical courts of Doctors' Commons by St Paul's (where marriage licenses were granted, one later to Mr Jingle); then as a reporter for the *Mirror of Parliament*, rising to earn five guineas a week on the *Morning Chronicle*. The taprooms and snuggeries, the gin and warm water, the papers of cigars, the hot or cold punch, the barrels of oysters, the cherry brandy, the strong beer 'served up in its native pewter' must have occasioned some agreeable literary research.

Sara Gamp was grotesque: childbeds, sickbeds and deathbeds were painless for her, with her protective umbrella and gin-bottle, her services relieving relatives of their harassments and messiness, at a cost of 'eighteen pence a day for working people, and three and six for gentlefolks', extra for night watching. But Jeremiah Cruncher in *A Tale of Two Cities*, odd-job man by day and bodysnatcher by night, looks a respectable gravedigger against the grotesque shadows of Burke and Hare in the Edinburgh moonlight.

In March 1850, Dickens inaugurated *Household Words*, to be like *Punch* but not funny, to improve people and society, and at tuppence a copy selling 40,000 a week. The grotesque wickedness of the world, for which Dickens was ever on the alert, moved him to urge the workers to rise against Parliamentary indifference amid the cholera epidemic of 1854. Typhoid and cholera, spread by faecally infected water, swept the towns of England annually like the summer rain. In 1847, 10,000 had died in London, particularly among the labouring classes. The cholera microbe being yet undiscovered, the effect of dirty water and bad drains upon its mortality was accepted by the public only as vaguely as the effect of the moon on its sanity. People did not care to be bullied into cleanliness. So the world's first revolution incited by plague failed to materialise.

Household Words in 1857 objected sedately to the Parliamentary muddle of bills, confounded by professional jealousies and vanities, which aimed to establish a medical *Register* for doctors and a General Medical Council to oversee their suitability to be named in it. Only a third of the nation's doctors had any qualifications at all, but as there were no cures for anything, except the hopeful course of Nature, this did not much matter. It harmlessly invited the generous application of quackery, soothsaying and benevolent humbug. The following year, the Medical Registration Act was passed, and henceforth doctors had to be educated, to take exams, and to behave themselves. *Household Words* continued its interesting articles on medical items, like influenza and deaths under chloroform, and had a go at Harley Street:

The houses in Celsus Row are tall and gloomy. The odour of quinquina, highly-dried sasaparilla, and bitter aloes, seems to float about in the atmosphere. The gaunt iron railings before the houses look like the staves of mutes divested of their crepe . . . The brass-plates as you advance upwards towards Incremation Passage are as brazen pages of the Medical Directory . . . Swathed and muffled figures emerge from cabs and totter feebly into the houses. Cabmen forbear to slang, and butcher-boys to whistle, in Celsus Row. You hear in fancy the scratching of pens writing prescriptions, the clinking of the guinea fee into the physician's hand, the beating of the pulse, the long-drawn sigh, the half-suppressed groan as the patient waits agonisingly for a verdict of life or death from the doctor's lips.

Otherwise, Dickens expressed his concern for the nation's health by chairing dinners to raise money for hospitals: the Great Ormond Street Hospital for Sick Children was a natural, and invoked from him the tear-wrenching story of an Edinburgh infant discarded in an egg box.

When he was five, living at Chatham on the Medway, Dickens suffered attacks of left-sided abdominal colic from a kidney stone. These spasms continued through childhood and at the blacking factory, until he grew into a young man obsessive about his cleanliness and fussy about his dress, to which he added a flannel belt for the kidney. He had six days in bed with renal colic in 1853, while writing *Bleak House*, and was prescribed Extractum Hyoscyami Liquidum, henbane in alcohol, a relaxant which cured him: but perhaps he passed the stone. In January 1861, he was struck with *tic douloureux*, trigeminal neuralgia, severe bouts of paroxysmal pain on the side of the face served by the fifth cranial nerve, provoked by cold winds or blowing your nose, its origin, and at the time its cure, unknown. It stayed with him until death.

Since his twenties he had piles, which bled. At twenty-eight, finishing *The Old Curiosity Shop*, he developed an anal fistula. This is an ulcer of the anal edge—bleeding, discharging, itchy, so painful that the patient embraces prolonged constipation. The fistula was excised in 1840, six years before the mercy of anaesthesia was bestowed upon the world via the Massachusetts General.

Early in 1865, Dickens got a bad left foot, ascribed first to walking in the snow and next to gout, the self-inflicted wound of the port-toping classes, necessitating the padded embroidered gout-stools of London clubs to raise the agonised swollen toes to the blissful horizontal. Two years later, he consulted Sir Henry Thompson, a urologist who had crushed the bladder stones of two kings, Leopold I and Napoleon III; founder of the Cremation Society and the Golder's Green Crematorium Co; a keen astronomer who presented a photographic telescope to the Greenwich Observatory; a painter at the Royal Academy, a connoisseur of Nankin china, host to the famous, subject of Millais, and like his patient a novelist. This worldly surgeon dismissed gout for erysipelas, an infection untainted with port. As there was no treatment, Dickens, always abstemious, continued spasmodically to be painfully lame, his foot bandaged and up on the sofa. For a man of his bustling activity, this was the shackles of Newgate Gaol.

In April 1851, Dickens rented Fort House at Broadstairs on the east tip of Kent, squashed between Margate and Ramsgate, three popular seaside resorts where the biting breezes from the North Sea, the chilly breakers upon the broad airy sands, the bleak amusements of the pier, the extravagance of the poky shops, the unsavouriness of the served-up food, the uncongeniality of the pubs, the gloom of the twisting streets, and the resentment of the inhabitants towards the visitors upon whom they gorge, demonstrate each summer the valuable insensitivity of the British towards discomfort. Dickens thought numbing Broadstairs bracing, and went every season. To do himself even more good, he took a cold morning shower, a difficult creation of sanitary engineering with tanks in the roof and hefty pipes, and he drank a pint of water on rising and retiring. At Fort House he began *Bleak House*, which it is now so fittingly named.

Dickens travelled with a medicine chest containing sal volatile, in case he felt faint, ether in case of neuralgia, and laudanum to raise his spirits. Again, nobody thought twice about swallowing opium: Dr J. Collis Browne's Chlorodyne and such cordials were downed as unhesitatingly as the morning tea; and Queen Victoria provided for her guests at Balmoral the popular Vin Mariani, a lavish solution of cocaine.

He carried also a flask of brandy, which came in useful on 6 June 1865, when the platelayers of the South Eastern Railway, unaware of the time of high tide at Folkestone, which determined the departure of the London boat-train, had removed the rails from its track at the pretty Kent village of Staplehurst. Ten died in the derailment. Dickens assuaged the injured, supplementing the brandy with water, improvising his top-hat as a pail. The accident marred his ten days in Boulogne with the actress Ellen Ternan, a relationship he desired his readers not to know about, the only physical sex contaminating his novels being Sam Weller kissing housemaids.

The medicine chest shortly demanded the inclusion of digitalis.

In 1866, he suffered attacks of palpitations and faintness, diagnosed as 'great irritability of the heart'. This was atrial fibrillation, bouts of irregular rhythm in the heart's upper chambers, which develop clots, which break up and lodge in the arteries of the brain, which cause strokes. He was advised to rest, whereupon he became a difficult patient, because his busy life was whirring faster than ever.

Their inescapable autobiographies indicate how famous actors yearn to be writers, though few writers hanker for the nightly exertion of being actors. Dickens was stage-struck. As a child, he had longed for the boards; at twenty he won an audition at the Covent Garden Theatre to do comic songs, but a bad cold put it off. The next year, he produced privately the opera *Clari*, or the *Maid of Milan* (he sang her Father, a Farmer). He ruthlessly dragooned his friends and house-guests into amateur dramatics. His production at the Duke of Devonshire's Piccadilly house in May 1851, of Sir Edward Bulwer Lytton's *Not So Bad As We Seem*, or *Many Sides To A Character* (Lord Wilmot, A young man at the head of the Mode more than a century ago, Mr Charles Dickens), the cast including Wilkie Collins and the Editor of *Punch*, was fittingly observed by Queen Victoria and Prince Albert.

In 1858, while ridding himself of his wife, Dickens visualised the beguiling combination of reading his works to an audience. *Pickwick* and the Christmas books were instant hits, four six-week tours each earning £5,000. In America in 1867 he was a riotous success. Boston was sold out, four performances for $16,000, nothing like culture. New York—whose citizens once massed on the waterfront, as the steamer docked with the next instalment of *The Old Curiosity Shop*, shouting to the bridge: 'Is Little Nell dead?'—pushed Dickens' American takings towards $200,000, plus a banquet at Delmonico's. But a one-man show running for ten years is hard work. The infection of his foot had flared again, he was exhausted and sleepless, he shuddered at railway journeys—reasonably, after Staplehurst.

At Birmingham in 1866, Dickens was billed for 'The trial of Mr Pickwick' but did *Nicholas Nickleby* instead, apologised, returned to the stage and gave them *Pickwick*. His memory became worse. He had impairment of vision and of speech—disastrously, he could not pronounce 'Pickwick'. His Dr Beard prescribed idleness. After a few days he was writing again, and in April 1869 was on his way to read to eager Blackpool. Reaching Chester, he became giddy, with weakness in his left hand and leg. It was the first of his TIAs, transient ischaemic attacks, the passing strokes sprung by the clots from his heart.

Dr Beard hastened from London, ordered cancellation of the readings and took him back to Harley Street and Sir Thomas Watson, aged seventy-seven, whose *Lectures on the Principles and Practice of Physic* enjoyed in the profession the popularity of the works of his patient. Sir Thomas found Dickens 'on the brink of an attack of paralysis of his left side, and possibly of apoplexy', caused by overwork, worry and excitement. He banned readings and railways. Dickens restlessly objected. A crammed hall applauding his entrance to the platform had become a glorifying addiction. And there was the money, too.

He agreed to postpone his next performance. He felt better already. Though inactivity would not have prolonged his life. Today, he would be filled with aspirin, antihypertensive and cardiac stabilising drugs. He went home to Gadshill near Rochester, the house where he had lived since 1856 and which he had coveted since boyhood. In the theatrical tradition, he announced his final appearance on any stage, a dozen readings early in snowy 1870 at St James's Hall in London (promptly, standing room only).

On 8 June, he was half way through writing *The Mystery of Edwin Drood* in the two-storey open-staircase Swiss chalet in his Gadshill garden. He returned to the house early at six o'clock, sat for dinner with his live-in sister-in-law Georgina Hogarth, turned ashen, babbled, announced that he was going to London, rose from the table, fell, was unconscious. The local doctor administered an enema and advised hot bricks for the cold feet. Dr Beard arrived, then a Harley Street physician (twenty guineas) who diagnosed an undoubted cerebral haemorrhage. The next evening, Dickens developed the premortal gasping breathing known to Hippocrates, at six he died, Millais arrived to do the drawing, and three days later he was buried in Westminster Abbey.

How many thousand faces must have passed before the doctor's eyes; how many pitiable tales of woe must have poured into his ears; what awful secrets must find a repository beneath that black satin waistcoat! We may lie to the lawyer, we may lie to the confessor, but to the doctor we cannot lie. The murder must out. The prodigal pressed for an account of his debts will keep one back; the penitent will hide some sin from his ghostly director; but from the doctor we can hide nothing, or we die. He is our greatest master here on earth. The successful tyrant crouches before him like a hound; the scornful beauty bows the knee; the stern worldly man clings desperately to him as the anchor that will hold him from drifting into the dark sea that hath no limits. The doctor knows not rank. The mutilated beggar in St Celsus's accident ward may be a more interesting case to him than the sick duchess. He despises beauty—there may be a cancer in its bloom. He laughs at wealth; it may be rendered intolerable by disease. He values not youth; it may be ripe for the tomb, as hay for the sickle. He makes light of power; it cannot cure an ache, nor avert a twinge of gout. He only knows, acknowledges, values, respects two things—Life and Death.

So said Dickens about doctors.
Leaving a nasty suspicion that so might have said Mr Pecksniff.

WALT WHITMAN

1819–1892

WALT WHITMAN was a valuable part of President Lincoln's medical establishment during the American Civil War of 1861–5.

He was the son of a small Long Island farmer of Quaker tendencies with a Dutch wife, who moved, when Walt was aged four, to Brooklyn village to become a builder. Walt, the second child of nine, was an office-boy at eleven, an errand-boy on the *Long Island Patriot* at thirteen, an itinerant school-teacher for five years, and at twenty-seven he was editing the Brooklyn *Eagle*. He was fired for worrying too much about the southern slaves, became a New York carpenter and at thirty-six published his book of poems, *Leaves of Grass*.

This went down with the literati like Mrs Squeers's morning brimstone and treacle with the scholars of Dotheboys Hall. But Emerson called it 'the most extraordinary piece of wit and wisdom that America has yet contributed,' and several anonymous laudatory reviews proclaimed things like: 'An American bard at last!'—but Whitman had written all these himself.

The poems had some hefty sexy bits:

> Love thoughts, love juice, love-odour, love-yielding, love-climbers, and
> > the climbing sap,
> Arms and hands of love, lips of love, phallic thumbs of love, breasts of
> > love,
> > bellies press'd and glued together with love.

And:

I pour the stuff to start sons and daughters for these States,
I press with slow rude muscles,
I brace mysef effectually, I listen to no entreaties,
I dare not withdraw till I deposit what has so long accumulated within me.

The slim volume of twelve poems achieved a literary success in London. It inflamed Anne, the widow of Blake's biographer Alexander Gilchrist, herself the authoress of the *Life of Mary Lamb*, who gushed to Whitman: 'It was the divine soul embracing mine. I never before dreamt what love meant.' The poet did not reply. She wrote effusive essays about him, usefully in the *Boston Radical*, and to his horror crossed the Atlantic in 1876 with three of her children to implement her passion in Philadelphia. But they settled their romance by taking tea together, she then being forty-eight, and he fifty seven and an enthusiastic homosexual.

For ten years Whitman was a clerk in the Department of Justice office in Washington. His former job in the Indian Bureau had ended abruptly in 1865, because of the dirty bits in *Leaves of Grass* (a friend promptly published a book in his defence, which, too, was later discovered to have been written by Walt Whitman). Walt fell for a Washington tram-driver, Peter Doyle, and sent him loving letters which were later published: 'Good night, my darling son—here is a kiss for you, dear boy . . . I often think of you, Pete, and put my arm around you, and hug you up close, and give you a good bus—often.' He wrote similarly to other youngsters; the mother of a later admirer, then a boy, was warned against letting her son too near 'the lecherous old man'. Whitman claimed to have several illegitimate children, but this falsity was uttered in the same carefree spirit that praised his own poems.

Walt's brother George joined up when the Civil War began, and in December 1862 was wounded. Walt ventured to the front, to find him recovering. He returned to Washington with a boatload of casualties. 'Beginning at first with casual visits to see some of the Brooklyn men, I became by degrees more and more drawn in, until I have now been for many weeks quite a devotee to the business—a regular self-appointed missionary to those thousands and tens of

thousands of wounded and sick young men here, left upon government hands, many of them languishing, many of them dying.'

For three years he was a volunteer nurse in Washington, or
across the Potomac at Fredericksburg, maintaining himself as a
sporadic war correspondent. He became an able dresser of wounds
in 'these hospitals, so different from all others, these thousands,
and tens and twenties of thousands of American young men, badly
wounded, all sorts of wounds, operated on, pallid with diarrhoea,
languishing, dying with fever, pneumonia, etc, open a new world
somehow. I sometimes put myself in fancy on the cot, with typhoid,
or under the knife.'

His fancies overtook him in July 1863. Assisting at the amputation of a gangrenous limb of a Union soldier from Virginia, 'to
whom he was much attached', he suffered a scalpel cut of his right
hand. The hand became infected with the virulent germ, red streaks
ran up the lymphatics to his shoulder. It was the risk that brought
to many surgeons frantic amputation at the elbow or shoulder, and
generally death from septicaemia, until antibiotics tamed it almost
a century later. Only two years afterwards, the accident killed Ignaz
Semmelweiss in Vienna, who had controlled the same deadly
process in childbirth through antiseptic hand-washing. Walt was
lucky, and recovered in a month.

Like our Miss Nightingale, Walt calculated that he found himself
'among from eighty thousand to one hundred thousand of the
wounded and sick, as sustainer of spirit and body in some slight
degree, in their time of need.'

Like her at Scutari, he discovered: 'The work of the army
hospital visitor is indeed a trade, an art, requiring both experience
and natural gifts, and the greatest judgment. A large number of
visitors do no good at all, while many of them do harm. The
surgeons have great trouble from them. Some visitors go from
curiosity—as to a show of animals. Others give the men improper
things. Then there are always some poor fellows, in the crises of
sickness of wounds, that imperatively need perfect quiet—not to
be talked to by strangers. Few realize that it is not the mere giving
of gifts that does good; it is the proper adaption.'

He found that most wounds reaching the camp hospitals were in the arms and legs: but perhaps those penetrating the body had already killed their victims. 'The prevailing maladies are typhoid fever, and the camp fevers generally, diarrhea, catarrhal affections and bronchitis, rheumatism, and pneumonia. These forms of sickness lead, all the rest follow. The deaths range from six to ten per cent of those under treatment.'

He was a systematic nurse. 'Bed 53 wants some liquorice; Bed 6—erysipelas—bring some raspberry vinegar to make a cooling drink; Bed 18 wants a good book—a romance.' He thought the army doctors inefficient and unsympathetic: they 'generally give too much medicine, oftener making things worse.'

At four in the morning of 23 January 1873, now a civil servant in Washington, he suffered a stroke with paralysis of his left side. For ten years, he had been complaining of occasional 'sun stroke' and 'aching and fullness of the head', which were probably transient ischaemic attacks in his brain. He had another stroke in July 1885, inciting his doctor to seek the opinion of Dr William Osler, the thirty-five-year-old Professor of Medicine at the University of Pennsylvania.

Sir William Osler, Baronet, from Bond Head, Ontario, observer of Osler's nodes on the finger-ends in heart disease, was the most glorious of the medical grandees who strode the wards of the nineteenth century. At twenty-five, he was professor at his own university, McGill in Montreal, at forty he was professor at Johns Hopkins and in 1904 Regius Professor at Oxford. He serenely dominated the Radcliffe Infirmary, where his handsome, walrus-moustached portrait continued gazing with benign authority at us young doctors snatching our meals.

A zealous attender of the post-mortem room, Osler rightly founded his medical practice on pathology, which is essentially the record of doctors' failures and mistakes. To a drunken beggar one freezing night Osler gave his overcoat, remarking: 'There is only one thing of value about you, and that is your hobnailed liver'— which he received, with his overcoat back, by the supplicant's scrawled directions a fortnight later, when the liver had killed him.

Osler had scant faith in drugs: 'Time, in divided doses,' was his favourite prescription. But there were few drugs of the slightest effectiveness for him to give. However impressive his diagnosis, however fluent his teaching, however arresting his philosophising, however inspiring his presence at the bedside for both patients and students, such qualities were as wasted as a Napoleon bereft of cannon and ammunition.

Osler turned to literature, medical and general, 730 books and articles in fifty years. He was an inspiring medical sermoniser, his *Principles and Practice of Medicine* was the New Testament to Gray's anatomical Old. He became a Christ Church don, a curator of the Bodleian Library and a director of the University Press. He was loaded with degrees, and esteemed an authority on Sir Thomas Browne, John Locke and Robert Burton of the *Anatomy of Melancholy*. Today, such a physician in the round is unknown. Happily, he has the means to busy himself curing many of our diseases, rather than displaying a knowledge of the classics which is better vouchsafed us by the classicists.

Dr Maurice Bucke of London, Ontario, exchanged telegrams with his friend Professor Osler in Philadelphia:

PLEASE SEE ME WALT AND LET ME KNOW HOW HE IS.

WHO IS WALT AND WHERE DOES HE LIVE?

This identification being resolved, Professor Osler encountered Walt Whitman at 238 Mickle Street, across the Delaware at Camden, New Jersey. He found him: 'With a large frame, and well-shaped, well-poised head, covered with a profusion of snow-white hair, which mingled on the cheeks with a heavy long beard and moustache, a fine figure of a man who had aged beautifully, or more properly speaking, majestically. The eyebrows were thick and shaggy, and the man seemed lost in a hirsute canopy.' He was a non-smoker, went easy on the whisky, and smelt of eau-de-Cologne. 'The machine was in fairly good condition considering the length of time it had been on the road,' Osler assured the patient grandly.

Osler discovered some 'transient indisposition which has passed away'; but three years later, he was called to diagnose the progressive paralysis which would kill him. Walt wanted this process to proceed in peace. 'Don't get a doctor,' he implored sensibly. 'If doctors come I shall not only have to fight the disease, but fight them, whereas if I am left alone, I have but one foe to contend with.' By now, Professor Osler was a Whitman fan. He found *Leaves of Grass* in his Philadelphia club library, and confessed it rough stuff on a palate which savoured Keats and Shelley. Dr Bucke enthusiastically corrected him over dinner that Walt Whitman was a genius: *Leaves of Grass* illuminated a blissful existence on a higher plane than humans customarily enjoyed. Thus encouraged, Osler visited Walt regularly until his death, and made nice remarks about the 'good grey poet' in *The Times* in 1919, six months before his own end.

Walt had a keen interest in anatomy, if selective. His poem *I Sing the Body Electric* is all about man-balls, man-root, the womb, the teats, love-perturbations and risings, the thin red jellies within you or within me, the bones and the marrow of the bones.

He made a difficult patient, with a watchful eye for his doctors.

Osler 'has made up some prescription of wine and cocoa which has helped me. He's a fine fellow, and a wise one, I guess: wise, I am sure—he has the air of assurance . . . He believes in the gospel of encouragement—on putting the best construction on things—the best foot forward.'

This is a sound bedside manner, which did not impress:

'I don't like his pooh-poohs: this professional air of a doctor grates me. It is like the case of a rich man who loses half a dollar and says grandly to the man who finds it: Never mind: keep it: I've lots more than I want. But the real man is Dr Bucke,' Walt decided. 'He is the top of the heap. He has such a clear head, such a fund of common sense—such steady eyes—such a steady hand.'

He concluded generously: 'But from the point of view of my own comfort I'm in a pretty boggy condition indeed. But so the doctor feels all right about it I don't suppose it matters what I feel. I like to see the doctors comfortable, anyway . . . Ah! these doctors! after all, do they know much? I love doctors and hate their medicine. I have no great faith in or fear of doctors—they don't seem to do much good or much harm.'

The final difficulty with Walt Whitman was discovering what he died of.

Apart from the residual paralysis of his strokes, he had suffered dyspepsia and an enlarged prostate, for which, recalling his wartime skills, he learnt to catheterise himself. The day after his death, on 27 March 1892, a post-mortem was done in the back parlour, strongly opposed by Mrs Davis, his housekeeper. The pathologist decided that Walt had perished from 'general miliary tuberculosis and parenchymatous nephritis. There was also found a fatty liver, gallstone, a cyst in the adrenal, tubercular abscesses, involving the bones, and pachymeningitis.'

A pathological museum in a skin. Professor Osler would have been more intrigued in his remains than in his verses.

Justly, Walt had come to complain that he was:

> . . . a batter'd, wreck'd old man,
> Sore stiff with many ills, sicken'd and nigh to death,
> Old, poor, and paralyzed.
> My hands, my limbs grow nerveless,
> My brain feels rack'd, bewildered.

The American Anthropometric Society got their hands on his brain, which weighed forty-five ounces. But in 1908: 'The brain of Walt Whitman, together with the jar in which it had been placed, was said to have been dropped on the floor by a careless assistant. Unfortunately, not even the pieces were saved.'

Here was a practical illustration of the stark corporeal humility expressed in the burial service. Walt Whitman would have made a wonderful poem of it.

BERNARD SHAW

1856–1950

GEORGE BERNARD SHAW presented doctors with a dilemma: Are we as good as we think we are?

Bernard Shaw was one of those irritating people who are never ill. A non-drinker, non-smoker and vegetarian, he was over six foot tall and as spare as a scarecrow, as austere in his habits as in mind. Born in Dublin—into the Irish gentry—the third child of a jolly, drunken member of the Corn Exchange and an unloved singing-teacher, he became a cashier at a land-agent's at £84 a year until his parents parted, when he left for London, aged twenty. He then lived on his mother for nine years, in which he earned £6, five of them from a patent medicine advertisement.

He became a dramatic critic who was generally more entertaining than his nightly subjects, at £6 a week. He had written eight comedies, but these had enraged either their first-night audiences or the censorial Lord Chamberlain, or had baffled the actors in rehearsal. In 1898 he suffered an unspecified mental illness which drove him from London, but by 1903 both his psychology and fortunes had recovered, and absolutely everybody was cramming into the Court Theatre in Sloane Square for *Major Barbara*.

Turned forty, he married Charlotte, a fellow Socialist of the Fabian Society. She was his only wife, and she spared him the distraction of children. He ended up as a Fabian squire, residing at 'Shaw's Corner' in the Hertfordshire village of Ayot St Lawrence, twenty miles north of London. He worked in the mornings, napped after lunch, and before retiring at eleven at night burst into song in his bedroom, his repertoire extending from opera to ballads, his range from soprano to double-bass.

One morning in 1943, he asked cheerfully during the conversation with a visitor to Ayot: 'Do you notice anything different about me today?'

'You have new shoes on.'

'Oh, no! They are at least ten years old. But I thought you might see something different about me today because I became a widower at 2.30 this morning.'

He observed a few days later: 'Cremation is not what it was. You can't see the body burned: it's a very unsatisfactory ceremony these days.'

He clearly shared a doctor's workmanlike view of life and death.

Aged eighty-six, Shaw was still shovelling the snow and mounting ladders pruning the plum-trees. Over a Sunday breakfast at Ayot in 1946, he announced to a friend: 'When I got up this morning I felt extremely queer. I've never felt quite like that before, and I'm sure I'm going to die.'

'How do you feel now?' she asked politely.

'Not so bad, but still rather queer.'

'Then you're all right. On the day you're going to die you'll get up feeling like a boy of ten,' she assured him cheerfully.

Four years later, he rose boyishly enough to climb ladders, but the plum-trees got him. He fell and fractured the neck of his femur, which no orthopedist could treat with optimism. He lay in bed and developed pulmonary emboli and perished.

Alive, he had refused a peerage, the Order of Merit and the Nobel Prize. Dead, he rejected the Hereafter. 'When I die, I die,' he stated flatly. This matches his fellow-nonagenarian Bertrand Russell's assertion: 'When I die I shall rot'. Perhaps by that age they had both grown utterly bored with themselves.

Because he was never ill, Bernard Shaw developed a fondness for doctors.

Anyone who has ever known doctors well enough to hear medical shop talked without reserve knows that they are full of stories about each other's blunders and errors, and that the theory of their omniscience and omnipotence no more holds good among themselves than it did with Molière and Napoleon.

He got his doctors' shop from St Mary's Hospital, beside the busily puffing Paddington station in west London. He possessed an equally talkative friend, Sir Almroth Wright, who was five years younger and qualified at Trinity College, Dublin, in 1883.

Sir Almroth Wright was the great immunizer. In the South African War of 1899–1902, typhoid killed twice as many British troops as the sharpshooting Boers. As Professor of Pathology at the Army Medical School, Wright abolished typhoid by injecting its attenuated germs to stimulate resistance. The army thought this operation as militarily dubious as the Charge of the Light Brigade. Wright left huffily in 1902, became Professor at St Mary's and was soon busily inoculating everybody within reach against anything which raised their temperature. Luckily, ten years was enough for the army to grasp a new idea, so in the Great War nobody died from typhoid at all.

Shaw often came to tea with Sir Almroth and his staff in the poky library of the St Mary's Inoculation Department, kettle hissing on gas-ring, tuberculin-tested milk in the jug. Shaw rewarded his teatime host by turning him into the satirical character Sir Colenso Ridgeon in *The Doctor's Dilemma*. Sir Almroth walked out of the first night at the Court Theatre in 1906, though not through affronted professional dignity, but because he objected to the plot.

The untroublesome patient Shaw faced the profession with some painful truths. He added to the text of *The Doctor's Dilemma* in 1911 an eighty-eight-page *Preface on Doctors*, which, like all his plays, still commands a critical eye: though hooking his ideas from the sparkling, frothy cascade of his prose makes difficult fishing.

It is not the fault of our doctors that the medical service of the community, as at present provided for, is a murderous absurdity.

To a socialist, setting the world aright—once justice is done to the deserving poor—is a task as straightforward as tidying the morning desk. Shaw's cure was removing the cash incentive for doctors to provide treatment. This was applied in Britain thirty-seven years later, and still gets its murderous absurdities in the papers every morning.

> The practicability of any method of extirpating disease depends not only on its efficacy, but on its cost.

We are just discovering this.

He judged severely:

> The medical profession has not a high character; it has an infamous character . . . The only evidence that can decide a case of malpractice is expert evidence: that is, the evidence of other doctors; and every doctor will allow a colleague to decimate a whole countryside sooner than violate the bond of professional etiquet by giving him away.

This defect has been over-generously overcome by the lawyers.

Shaw's contribution to the mythology of pathology was the 'nuciform sac', a nonexistent congenital abnormality which every private patient was eagerly advised to have removed. Shaw's complaint that operations had fashions, like skirts and sleeves, is still a just one—despite the unimaginable elaboration of the dress-making. In 1911, the surgeons were virtuously snipping off tonsils and uvulas in the throat. In 1921, they were more dramatically removing floating kidneys. In 1931, it was pockets of pus. In 1941, they were ripping out chains of sympathetic nerves. Other organs have continued to enjoy a passing modishness, but we shall have to wait another ten years before we can raise our eyebrows at those which are chic today.

> I presume nobody will question the existence of a widely spread popular delusion that every doctor is a man of science . . . Doctoring is an art, not a science.

The only art in doctoring is that of applying science to the patient. Medicine was becoming generally scientific at the start of the century, particularly through the work of Sir Almroth Wright, which Shaw refreshingly approved. In 1928, Shaw would have shared the teatime biscuits with Professor Alexander Fleming, smoking away on the library settee. Fleming's discovery that penicillin mould ate germs (which occurred when he was away on holiday in Scotland) inspired Professor Florey at Oxford in 1940 to manufacture the drug penicillin. This initiated the age of antibiotics, which rendered Sir Almroth's life's work on immunisation redundant. Or did it? We are not so sure, now the germs are getting the better of the antibiotics. Unlike Leonardo da Vinci painting the Mona Lisa, doctors inspired by science cannot create medicine—or their immortality by making it up as they go along.

> Virginia Snake Root fascinates the imagination of the herbalist as mercury used to fascinate the alchemists. On week days he keeps a shop in which he sells packets of pennyroyal dandelion, &c., labelled with little lists of the diseases they are supposed to cure, and apparently do cure to the satisfaction of the people who keep on buying them. I have never been able to perceive any distinction between the science of the herbalist and that of the duly registered doctor.

Snake Root continues to fascinate. Herbalism is now dignified as alternative medicine.

> Public support of vivisection is founded almost wholly on the assurances of the vivisectors that great public benefits may be expected from the practice. Not for a moment do I suggest that such a defence would be valid even if proved . . . I would rather swear fifty lies than take an animal which had licked my hand in good fellowship and torture it.

Antivivisectionists prefer children to die from a disease rather than animals to die in discovering its cure. We would risk our lives to grab a child running about a busy motorway; we should jib at risking it for a straying dog; we should not contemplate it for a rabbit, even if we could catch it; hedgehogs and toads are squashed unnoticeably. 'I'm not just one of those fools who think that one life is as good as another, simply because it is a life; that a grasshopper is as good as a dog and a dog is as good as a man. You must recognize a hierarchy of existences,' Aldous Huxley was putting Shavians to shame in 1925.

The word of Shaw:

> Do not try to live for ever. You will not succeed.

Quite right.

> The doctor never hesitates to claim divine omniscience.

Quite wrong.

> [The doctor's] reputation stands, like an African king's palace, on a foundation of dead bodies.

Quite right. It makes us humbly aware of our limitations. But was Shaw aware of his own?

> For example, just at present the world has run raving mad on the subject of radium, which has excited our credulity precisely as the apparitions at Lourdes excited the credulity of Roman Catholics.

Not bloody likely.

MARCEL PROUST

1871–1922

READING PROUST'S *A la recherche du temps perdu* is like swimming the Channel from Cap Gris Nez to Dover on a warm day.

It is a novel of one and a quarter million words, demanding 3,000 comfortably legible pages. It was published between 1913 and 1927, in seven parts. The first section, *Du côté de chez Swann*, appeared from a 'vanity press' at the author's expense, to widespread disinterest. The second, *A l'ombre des jeunes filles en fleurs*, won the 1920 Prix Goncourt. The Goncourt is the star of the thousand literary prizes by which France displays its steadfast championship of culture, and is fittingly presented at an excellent restaurant near the place de l'Opéra.

Proust's father Arien was Professor of Medicine at the University of Paris. He was a tallow-chandler's son from Illiers-Combray near Chartres, who qualified in 1862 with a thesis on spontaneous pneumothorax—lung collapse, often causing sudden death. He became *chef de clinique* at the Charité Hospital in 1863, when the latest cholera epidemic was threatening France.

This deadly disease of torrential diarrhoea had first invaded Europe from Asia thirty years earlier. Heinrich Heine has described arrival of the *guillotine ambulante* in Paris in 1832: a harlequin collapsed at a masked *mi-carême* ball, his mask was torn off, his face was violet, his limbs deathly cold, panic-stricken carriages clattered to the Hôtel Dieu, dead dancers were buried in their dominoes, bodies crammed the public halls, to be hastily coffined by sewing into sacks, the hearses were queuing up at the Père Lachaise cemetery, 120,000 of the rich jostled for passports at the Hôtel de Ville to flee the city, six suspected mass-poisoners were hanged *à la lanterne* and dragged naked through the streets, the rag-pickers rioted at official deprivation of their rubbish tips, but the government ventured to do nothing more drastic because it would be bad for business.

To prevent repetition of such disruptions to Parisian life, the Second Empire dispatched Professor Proust in 1869 to St Petersburg and Constantinople, then on horseback to Persia (the Shah gave him a carpet). He was tracing backwards the infective spoor of the *Vibrio cholerae*, the microbe which still awaited discovery by Robert Koch in Egypt in 1883. Professor Proust knowledgeably identified Egypt as Europe's gateway for cholera, and planned a *cordon sanitaire* with quarantine for travellers. The English, who ran Egypt, demolished the scheme as another shifty example of the French nosing their way into Suez (they were probably right).

Professor Arien Proust was a handsome, solid man with a fluffy beard, who married the fifteen-years-younger Jeanne Weil in Paris in September 1870. This was the month in the Franco-Prussian war when the Germans began their siege, which ended with the Parisians supposedly eating their cats and mice. The revolutionary Paris Commune was demolished in May 1871, with 17,000 shot in the streets, and on 10 July Marcel was born. Two years later came his brother Robert, who became Professor of Surgery at Paris and wrote the more useful *Surgery of the Female Genital Organs*.

Madame Proust was Jewish, but being pressingly rich was ensured reception in the Paris salons. Marcel in his twenties—dark, handsome, heart-faced with a wisp of moustache—was into the salon circuit. *Espièglerie* sparkled like the champagne, *esprit* fluttered like the napkins, *bons mots* were passed round like the *petits fours*, literary *bavardage* circulated as incessantly as the footmen, and there was no need to grieve over the brilliance of your unuttered *esprit de l'escalier* because you could always work it into your next book.

Proust's edible inspiration for *A la recherche du temps perdu* approaches the familiarity of Newton's for gravity. The novel's Narrator—which is Proust but not quite—arriving home one dreary winter's afternoon, is offered by his mother a cup of tea and a madeleine. These are dull little yellowish cakes made of butter, sugar, flour and eggs, shaped like scallop shells and tasty only when accompanying spiced fruits cooked in red wine. Dipping his cake in his tea—which no Englishman would be seen doing—he shudders as:

> An exquisite pleasure had invaded my senses, something isolated, detached, with no suggestion of its origin. And at once the vicissitudes of life had become indifferent to me, its disasters innocuous, its brevity illusory—this new sensation having had on me the effect which love has of filling me with a precious essence; or rather this essence was not in me, it was me. I had ceased now to feel mediocre, contingent, mortal. Whence could it have come to me, this all-powerful joy? I sensed that it was connected with the taste of the tea and the cake, but that it infinitely transcended these savours, could not, indeed, be of the same nature.

The episode is complicated by Proust deriving *his* inspiration for the account of *this* inspiration one snowy night in 1909, coming home freezing to his apartment in the boulevard Haussmann. He was prevailed upon by his amiable housekeeper Céleste to take a cup of tea instead of his customary coffee, into which he dipped a fragment of dry toast, which less sweetly evoked suddenly the joyful, orange-blossom-scented memories of his childhood.

Marcel Proust suffered from mother-fixation. During his childhood summers, the family moved from central Paris to suburban Auteuil south of the Bois de Boulogne, father catching the bus to the grands boulevards every morning to work. When Marcel was tucked-up at night, mother would read to him—a favourite was George Sand's *François le Champi*, about a lad abandoned in the fields (*un champi*), who is picked up by a girlish *femme de meunier*, who in untimely widowhood later enjoys his love. Mother would then give Marcel a good-night kiss and blow out the candle.

One night, when he was seven, she had a dinner-party and forgot him. Gazing down, as children do, at the curious sight of noisy adults with their noses in liqueur glasses in the garden, the slighted child opened his window and yelled for mother. Unwillingly, she tore herself away from her guests. Marcel greeted her with hysterics. She explained to her visitors that it was his nerves, the child just didn't know *what* he wanted. This incident was the fly in the polished amber of Proust's memories. It taught him that love and happiness are unreliable. He passed his life trying to prove otherwise, but failed. Ah, well.

Sigmund Freud was then aged twenty-two, a scholar at the Vienna Institute of Physiology, performing research into some unusual cells in the spinal cord of primitive fish. It was twenty years before Freud promulgated the Oedipus complex, by which every boy wishes to kill his father and sleep with his mother, to avoid which father desires to castrate him. In practice, such alarming behaviour does not intrude into everyday family life. But: 'To describe the mother-son tie in as idealistic terms as Freud did is simultaneously to deny a woman the right to have full sexual gratification with her husband.'

From the germinal Oedipus complex sprout the commonplace loves and jealousies, hates and rivalries among adults; and the weeds of various neuroses, the seeking the love of a mother-substitute and revenge on a father-substitute. Proust was an uncamouflaged homosexual—a 'Saturnian' he preferred to call it—occasioned by his emotional adherence to his mother. This subconsciously rendered copulation with any other female an act of incest.

André Gide, who published Proust in his avant-garde *Nouvelle Revue Française* before the war, suffered the same joyless inhibition. To Gide, Proust disclosed his liking for seeking orgasms by sticking hatpins into caged rats. Rats have a strong homosexual connection. This was being observed at the time by Freud in the 'Rat Man', an Austrian officer disablingly obsessed with the rumoured Chinese torture of a pail of rats strapped to his buttocks, gnawing their way inside until their whiskers appeared from his anus. Another contemporary, Oscar Wilde, Proust met over dinner in 1894; but they did not know what to make of one another.

More discomforting for Proust than homosexuality was a lifelong affliction with asthma. He generously spread his disease among the doctors he met by the dozen in his father's drawing-room, simultaneously collecting their oddities to create the doctors of his novel. Then in November 1903, the Professor fatally collapsed in the loo at the Ecole de Médicine, and two years later the beloved mother died from uraemia.

A doctor whom Proust had first consulted in his twenties informed him that asthma was a neurotic condition, and suggested a Swiss sanatorium where they would break him of the asthma habit as they broke other inmates of the morphia habit. Another doctor in 1905 guaranteed cure from three months' isolation in his own nursing-home on the Left Bank; another from six weeks at *his* nursing-home by the Bois de Boulogne, which the patient accepted, without noticeable effect. A further doctor advised bed rest interrupted with cold baths and no alcohol. The author of *Hygiene for Asthmatics* did him no good at all. A family friend, Dr Robin, refused to treat him, because his asthma was an emotional outlet which spared him from developing other hypochondriacal states.

Proust had the shallow, attention-seeking, manipulative personality of hysteria, which mimics illness for its own ends. He was like the young Frenchwoman who affected paralysis to avoid a loveless marriage, the case which inspired Freud. Proust's joy—on the unforgettable night of the forgotten kiss—that his deliberate paddy should be ascribed to the perfectly excusable, understandably uncontrollable, childhood 'nerves', is the delight felt by the hysteric: 'I could weep henceforth without sin'. He was neurotic, but his asthma was not.

The asthma attacks started each April, provoked by an allergy to pollens, which today would be treated with an aerosol inhaler spraying a bronchial dilator and an anti-allergic steroid. Proust sensibly tried to protect himself from the pollens with closed windows. He augmented this defence with a cork lining to his bedroom, when he moved into the first-floor flat at 102 boulevard Haussmann, near the Gare St Lazare. (His surplus furniture from the parental home he gave to a favourite footman, who had launched out to run a male brothel round the corner in the rue de l'Arcade.)

The cork was useful also to keep out the noise, as he had taken the habit of working all night and sleeping from noon until the evening, when Céleste would bring his coffee and the day's *Le Figaro*, to which he was a stylish contributor. Cork also provided excellent acoustics. In the winter of 1916, Proust fell in love with the music of César Frank played by a male quartet, or possibly he fell in love with the viola player, or perhaps all four. He had them play to him alone after midnight within his constricting cork walls, encored them, commissioned more, and sustained them with champagne and *pommes frites* served by Céleste in black silk and a lace apron. He planned taking them to play intimately in Venice, but the war was a distraction, and his love cooled. The dimmed streets of Paris became sporadically bombed by Gothas, and in 1918 shelled by Big Bertha. In the spring of 1919, Proust left the boulevard Haussmann, and the walls were sold for bottle corks.

In June 1917, Proust consulted at La Salpêtrière Dr Joseph Babinski, whose sole-of-the-foot reflex placed his name on the lips of every medical student in the world. Proust invited him to trephine his skull for brain disease: Dr Babinski disagreed. In the summer of 1922, Proust was having severe attacks of asthma. That winter he caught pneumonia, developed a pulmonary abscess, suffered the useless cuppings and stimulant injections, sent out to the Ritz for an iced beer, and in the company of his brother Robert died at three in the afternoon of 18 November.

A la recherche du temps perdu is 'the supreme novel cycle of modern times'. I opened it long ago, but I regret to confess that somewhere south of the Godwin Sands I sank.

THE ARTS

$\mathcal{S}$ARAH $\mathcal{B}$ERNHARDT

1845–1923

'THERE ARE FIVE KINDS of actresses', pontificated Mark Twain, 'bad actresses, fair actresses, good actresses—and then there is Sarah Bernhardt.' Gushed a critic: 'She was more than an empress, she was a kind of divinity'. More gratifyingly, a worshipful public hosannaed reliably at the box-office: 'Divine Sarah!'

Sarah Bernhardt was born in Paris, the daughter of a Le Havre magistrate and a Berlin milliner, a Jewess. She went on the stage at thirteen and at seventeen joined the Comédie-Française. This stately institution had been founded in 1680 by the remnants of Molière's players (Molière achieved his ultimate theatrical irony by dying, after a massive pulmonary haemorrhage on stage, while playing *le malade imaginaire*).

The Comédie-Française was reorganised, along with the French church, courts, local government, education, national bank and Legion of Honour by Napoleon. The imperial impresario produced a theatrical co-operative, the young actors being allowed to choose their first part, and if successful becoming rep players awaiting fame as the old stagers were pensioned off or died. Napoleon had other things on his mind at the time, being on his way to Moscow in 1812.

Sarah Bernhardt was slight, redheaded, dark-eyed, with the famous *voix d'or*, capricious and emotional. She blew stormily across the stuffy boards of the Comédie-Française because she was too good for them. She left to sing in burlesque, but flopped. She returned after the Franco-Prussian war of 1870 with a smash hit as Cordelia in the French *King Lear*. She did Cleopatra and Lady Macbeth, and in 1899 enjoyed a transvestite triumph as Hamlet, inciting the *Punch* cartoon of Sir Henry Irving playing opposite as

Ophelia. 'The only tribute a French translator can pay Shakespeare is not to translate him—even to please Sarah,' Max Beerbohm was grumbling. As a matter of course, she magnificently played Racine and Victor Hugo. She went into theatre management in Paris and opened her own *théâtre de boulevard*, the Sarah-Bernhardt in the place du Châtelet. She left to tour London and America, and made loads of money. In 1882 she married a Greek actor, with theatrical brevity.

In 1885 she toured South America, pursing a million francs. Homeward bound from Chile to Le Havre, she slipped on board and injured her right knee. The ship's doctor treated it with *pointes de feu*, slivers of burning wood applied round the joint, a treatment continued by her doctor at home. It would have the soothing warmth of short-wave diathermy, if more alarming.

The knee grew worse, walking was painful, but her profitability being matched by her extravagance she could not afford to retire. She acted either sitting down or using the stage furniture as crutches. By August 1914 she was chairbound, living on the boulevard Péreire on the edge of Paris, where Senator Georges Clemenceau passed her the Boches' blood-curdling compliment of planning to take her hostage and remove her to Berlin on their arrival in the Champs-Élysées. She decided on evacuation to her villa outside Bordeaux (it was difficult finding a taxi to the station, all being commandeered for troops to the Marne).

On 7 August she had gained temporary relief through the leg being immobilised in plaster by Dr Pozzi, an 'adored friend' in whom she expressed her faith by always addressing him as *Docteur Dieu*. Six months later the cast was still on, the leg worse, the skin abraded, and she wrote imploring Dr Dieu for an above-knee amputation. She was seventy-four, and reckoned coolly that she still had left in her ten years of—at least—sedentary poetry readings. If he refused to operate, she would fire a bullet into her knee, then he would have to. 'My friend, don't think I'm hysterical,' she assured him.

Potential amputees can have an odd insistence. Surgeons were once implored by patients to remove limbs paralysed by polio, because all the failures and torments of their lives arose from this useless flesh. The wise surgeon refused, knowing that the failures and torments would afterwards be blamed on some other bit of the body. Sarah Bernhardt won by presenting her family and Dr Dieu with an ultimatum: amputation or suicide.

The operation was planned in Bordeaux Hospital, to be performed by Major Denucé. Sarah telegraphed Dr Dieu in Paris of her agony, her inability to swallow more analgesics, she begged an urgent end to her useless torture, even by a day. She wired all her friends:

SO HAPPY MY LEG IS TO BE CUT OFF TOMORROW.

The case was becoming dramatic.

Mlle Coignt, the anesthetist, left an operation note which invites scripting.

Un Coup de Théâtre

10 a.m., Monday, 22 February 1915. The STAR enters the theatre. She is lying on a trolley, humming the Marseillaise.

Costume: White satin peignoir and pink crêpe-de-chine veils.

STAR: (*To Major Denucé.*) My darling, give me a kiss. (*To Mlle Coignt.*) Mademoiselle, I am in your hands. Promise you'll really put me to sleep. Let's go, quickly, quickly.

(MLLE COIGNT *places a mask, which delivers ether, over the* STAR'S *nose and mouth.*)

I'm choking, I'm suffocating, take it off!

(MLLE COIGNT *anxiously consults her apparatus, which is operating normally.*)

I'll never fall asleep. Why this ether? Chloroform would be

better. Ah! That's good. It's working, it's working, I'm going, I'm going, I'm gone . . .

(THE STAR *sleeps*. A PROFESSOR *takes her pulse and nods.* THE STAR *is placed on the theatre table.* MAJOR DENUCÉ *and his assistant* DR ROBERE *cut above the knee into the leg, which in five minutes drops off. The blood is stanched.* THE STAR *exits on the trolley.*)

STAR. (*Screaming.*) I want my beloved son, Maurice, my darling child!

MAURICE: (*Kissing her.*) Maman, you look splendid!

STAR: Where is the young woman who put me to sleep?

MLLE COIGNT: Madame, here I am.

STAR: Ah, darling, you're nice. Come here, I want to see you. Darling, I like you, stay a bit longer. Oh, how I'm suffering, how I'm suffering.

(*She recovers swiftly, and sends for her make-up.*)

Sarah escaped the oddity of a phantom limb, a persistent pain located in the flesh which has vanished. Acting being perfectly possible on one leg—look at *Treasure Island*—the next clinical task was finding her a wooden one. Sarah had difficulty choosing a limb to match her stump. She had constructed for herself a Sedan chair of cane and white wood, insertable into a car or a lift, and returned to face her breathless public. Eugène Morand had written her a one-acter, *Les Cathédrales*, in which she could play Strasburg Cathedral, sitting down.

One London friend in 1921 described Sarah:

As she lay back in the carriage, extravagantly pale, and with the lamp-black an inch thick under her eyes and on her eyelids, she looked lovelier than the fairest beauty of the season.

And another:

An elaborate *couvre-pied* hid her lower half. Her red hair was dye-streaked: her famous smile, smeared with sanguinary lipstick, displayed her yellow teeth, her clawlike hands were ill manicured and increased her resemblance to a tigress.

Sarah was haunted by a more murderous familiar than a chronic arthritic knee.

In 1898 and 1907 she had abdominal operations. In America in 1916, Dr Burger removed stones from her defective kidney, and on the ninth day post-op she developed uraemia. In Saratoga in the spring of 1917, she again suffered from uraemia, necessitating blood transfusions, for which a large proportion of the United States population volunteered. In Paris in 1922, she collapsed on the set while filming *La Voyante*. Her kidneys were failing. At 8 a.m. on 26 March 1923, her doctor announced through her window to the Press—whose anticipated jamming of the street outside she had inquired about—'Messieurs, Mme Sarah Bernhardt is dead.'

She continued to live on stage. Before the curtain rises in France, the stage manager performs the traditional three loud raps on the boards to secure the audience's attention, henceforth to be greeted by devotees of the amputee: '*Voici Sarah!*'

ℕICOLO ℙAGANINI

1782–1840

PAGANINI BECAME a difficult patient only when he was dead.

He was born in Genoa, his father Antonio was in the shipping trade, and his pious mother was informed by an angel in a dream that he would become the greatest violinist ever. He swiftly mastered the mandolin. He was instructed in the violin by the *maestro di cappella* of the Cathedral of San Lorenzo, and from the age of eleven was cheering up the congregation with his virtuoso solos every Sunday.

At fifteen, his father took him on tour, playing to the cities of Lombardy. He had three quiet years in Tuscany, composing for the violin and guitar, and in 1805 began eight years as musical director at the Court of Napoleon's sister, the Princess of Lucca and Piombo, later Grand Duchess of Tuscany. In 1815, he began a liaison with the Venetian dancer Antonia Bianchi, which produced a son, Anchillino, in 1826.

In 1813, Paganini had begun the concert tours which turned his life into a triumphant procession across Europe. In Vienna, his portraits and busts were sold in the streets, and clothes, perfumes, jewels, trinkets, even cakes, were profitably endorsed with his name. His wizardry at the King's Theatre had a London mob touching him to see if he was real. He made £17,000 from a year in England, though there was a joke:

> 'Who are these who pay five guineas
> To hear this tune of Paganini's?'
> Answering pun: 'Pack o'ninnies.'

Paganini was an odd sight on stage, tall, scraggy, gaunt-faced with long dark hair, bemoaned by the public as a living skeleton. He was a gambler, who once had to pawn his violin to pay his debts, but a French merchant replaced it with the Guarneri now lying in Genoa town hall. His 'Casino Paganini', established in Paris, crashed in 1838. He bowed happily to the publicity claiming that his abnormal skills indicated an alliance with the devil, and to the story that made him a convicted murderer, who had learnt the violin in jail, where they could provide only one string.

In Paris, Paganini asked Berlioz for something to play on his Stradivarius viola, was presented with *Harold in Italy*, but turned it down as not offering a big enough part. He is echoed respectfully in the piano music of Schumann, Liszt, Brahms and Rachmaninoff. In 1820, he published his twenty-four Caprices, Opus 1, which explored absolutely everything which anyone could possibly do with a violin. But otherwise he kept his scores as close as his instrument, not caring to lose his secrets and lower his price.

After six years on tour, he retired to Parma. He had been ill, and felt nostalgia for his native Genoa. He took the boat, but ended in Nice, where aged fifty-six he died of tuberculosis, in the rue de la Préfecture, separated by the flower market from the sea.

His itinerant existence then resumed.

Though the Pope had given him the Order of the Golden Spur in 1827, Paganini was unforceful in his religious opinions and undemonstrative in their observances. He had overlooked, or was denied, the last rites of the Church. His corpse would have been a trespasser on consecrated ground. The day after his death, his coffin was moved to a nearby tailor's at the junction of the rue Saint-Réparate, which runs inland towards the shops, and left in a cellar rented by an accommodating hatter.

It was moved next to a private apartment in a Nice hospital. Paganini's son Achillino—to whom he had left £80,000—had meanwhile started proceedings against the inhospitable bishop. He lost. He appealed. The case went to the Papal Court in Rome, the body of contention now lying in the lazaretto at Villefranche, just along the Corniche road to Monte Carlo. After a month, people began complaining about the smell. The body was removed from the company of the pestiferous and the quarantined, and put out on the beach, at the edge of the tideless Mediterranean.

One night, five of Paganini's friends, incited by such careless treatment of a dead genius, gathered up the coffin and carried it by torchlight round the adjacent Golfe de St Hospice to the point of the Cap. They buried it at the edge of sea, beside the landmark of an old round tower, and sealed the grave with a stone slab. The maestro had then been dead a year.

But the disappointed son shortly decided to remove the body to Paganini's birthplace of Genoa. He chartered a boat, dug up the coffin and gingerly laid it on deck. The Genoese quarantine officers refused to let it land, nor its living attendants, because the ship had sailed from Marseilles, and Marseilles had the cholera. The vessel set about and made for Cannes, which was equally unwelcoming. The Lérin Islands, to be viewed from the Croisette, then received the body, because there was no one there to object.

Four years Paganini lay buried on a lonely island rock, Sainte Ferréol, under another stone. Then he went back to Parma.

His son had chafed at leaving the idol of Europe in so forsaken a niche for eternity. He was buried more companionably in his own garden. Eight years later, he was dug up and re-embalmed. Twenty-three years afterwards, the Pope relented. Paganini was dug up again and entombed in Parma's church of Madonna della Staccata. He had then been dead only twenty years less than he had been alive.

He still did not rest in peace.

In 1893, doubt fell on the body's identity. A Hungarian violinist was sure that the venerated remains were of an impostor. The coffin was opened. The sixty-seven-year-old son recognised his father's tattered black coat, also 'the gaunt, thin face, the side whiskers and the long hair that fell over the neck and covered the white bones of the shoulder and the gleaming ribs'.

A virtuoso farewell performance.

The story was told by Sir Frederick Treves, Baronet, of the London Hospital, who in 1902 postponed King Edward VII's coronation to operate on his acute appendix, and who made a hit in the West

End and on Broadway fifty years after his death with *The Elephant Man*, whom he had discovered, reclaimed and nurtured. At the age of fifty-five, Sir Frederick rightly decided to abandon saving even royal lives, and passed his remaining fifteen years writing books amid the mimosa in the sunshine on the slopes of the Alpes-Maritimes, enjoying the *bouillabaisse*, *vins de Provence* and *salles de jeu* of the Côte d'Azur.

$\mathcal{V}$AN $\mathcal{G}$OGH

1853–1890

In 1993, Vincent van Gogh's *Flowering Garden* was sold in the United States for $40 million. His *Wheatfield and Cypresses at the Haute Galline*—a gift to the New York Metropolitan Museum of Art—went for $57 million. The price of his *Garden at Auvers* in Paris was a ridiculous $7.5 million, through its not having an export licence, but it was valued by the French courts at $50 million. His *Landscape with Rising Sun* shortly changed galleries for $50 million. In New York in 1995, the fashionable London auctioneers Christie's knocked down the small-sized *Boy with Blue Hat* for $13 million, while their rivals Sotheby's disposed of *Sous-bois* for $27 million.

Half a dozen pictures, occupying a total wall space of 19.32 square metres, made $210 million, or £315 million, in a couple of years.

The mind of the industrious artist must have boggled in paradise, having during his lifetime a century before sold frugally only one painting.

Vincent Willem van Gogh was born at Zundert, a small Dutch border town thirty miles south of Rotterdam. He was the eldest of the Calvinist pastor's six children, born exactly a year after a stillborn son also named Vincent Willem. He turned into a quiet child with a bad temper. At sixteen, his uncle found him a job with the fashionable art dealers Goupil & Co in The Hague, who sent him to their headquarters in Paris then in 1873 to the England of Millais, Rossetti, Gladstone, *Under the Greenwood Tree*, young Lillie Langtry, the Dolly Varden hat, Votes for Women, the Empire, the British and Foreign Temperance Society, the London Underground, pea-soupers, roller-skating 'rinkomania' and absolutely everyone for tennis.

He loved London. He earned £90 a year, wore a top-hat, thought Rotten Row with its hundreds of ladies and gentlemen on horseback one of the finest sights he had seen, discovered Shakespeare and saw all the art galleries and Madame Tussaud's. His workplace was off the Strand and his lodgings off Clapham Road, in Lambeth south of the Thames. 'I have a delightful home . . . I have nature and art and poetry. If that is not enough, what is?' he wrote in the earliest of his flowing letters to his brother Theo. His home was so delightful that he proposed to his landlady's daughter, but she turned him down. He grew sullen, withdrawn and awkward, and in 1876 Goupil fired him for being rude to the customers.

He became an unpaid schoolteacher in Ramsgate, the seaside resort where young Queen Victoria caught typhoid, across the chilly tip of Kent from Broadstairs, the bracing spot where Dickens appropriately wrote *Bleak House*. What van Gogh taught is unknown, though the demand for Dutch in Ramsgate must have been unpressing. He recorded reading the Bible to the scholars daily, and that his bedroom crawled with bugs but the sea view made him forget them. Headmaster Mr Stokes shortly moved his school to Twickenham Road in Isleworth, over the Thames from Kew Gardens. Van Gogh shortly moved himself to the nearby school of the Rev Thomas Slade-Jones, who was a Congregationalist Minister, and got religion.

On the last Sunday in October 1876, van Gogh preached at Richmond Methodist Church. His text was: 'I am a stranger in the earth, hide not Thy commandments from me', Psalm 119:19. His sermon was 3,500 words, half an hour in delivery. His theme was our pilgrims' progress through life (he had discovered Bunyan also). He found this a twisting and bleak road. 'Sorrow is better than joy—and even in mirth the heart is sad—and it is better to go to the house of mourning than to the house of feasts, for by the sadness of the countenance the heart is made better.' He rubbed in: 'And then, slowly but surely the face that once had the early dew of morning, gets its wrinkles, the hair turns grey or we lose it.' Such rambling gloom in a Dutch accent from an earnest twenty-three-year-old, when it was getting on for Sunday dinner, made a valuable test of pious attention and respect.

At Christmas, he went home to his family at Etten, east of Arnhem, and was lost to our monochromic land for good.

In the New Year, van Gogh crossed Holland to work in a Dordrecht bookshop, but by Easter he was fired. Suffering depression and an obsession with religion, he became a theological student at Amsterdam. His melancholy deepened, his face sagged despairingly, by night he inflicted self-flagellation, like St Francis of Assisi. The next year, he joined the School of Evangelism at Brussels, became a Christian communist and lived as a missionary among the coal-miners at Wasmes, near Mons. He was now becoming noticeably odd. His home was a hut, he slept on straw, his clothes were ragged, his food sparse and he never washed. In 1880, he decided to give up religion to be an artist instead, and instantly was far more cheerful.

Van Gogh studied drawing in Brussels, still solitary and intro-verted. He was matrimonially turned down again, by his widowed cousin Kee Vos—so decisively, that whenever he entered his family home, she left it. 'Let me see her for as long as I can keep my hand in the flame,' he implored, thrusting his fingers into the lamp. He had a row with his father about churchgoing, left home and caught gonorrhoea from a drunken prostitute in The Hague, ex-seamstress Sien Hoornik. He was treated by bed-rest—reading *Edwin Drood*—interrupted by quinine and alum enemas, and like Boswell he developed a urethral stricture requiring regular painful 'sounding' with a curved metal dilator. Perhaps he caught syphilis from her as well.

'I know full well that, frankly speaking, prostitutes are bad, but I feel something human in them which prevents me from feeling the slightest scruple about associating with them; I see nothing very wrong in them. I haven't the slightest regret about any past or present association with them. If our society were pure and well regulated, yes, then they would be seducers; but now, in my opinion, one may often consider them more as sisters of charity,' he wrote to Theo.

He lived happily with Sien and her five-year-old daughter for two years, during which she—probably they—had a son, Willem. He drew her pregnant, with long black hair, head in hands, skinny, big-bellied, large-rippled breasts already like feeding-bottles, and called it *Sorrow*. His family was now planning to commit him to an asylum. He left Sien, grew depressed and anxious and painted gloomy pictures of peasants, like his first masterpiece *The Potato Eaters*. He wanted to emphasise how the hands of this odd quintet, supping off potatoes and tea in the dim lamplight, had honestly dug the earth to earn their food. The picture was a compliment to manual labour.

In 1886, after a few months in Antwerp at the Academy of Fine Arts, he joined his brother Theo in Paris, unannounced. He was suffering stomach-aches and ten of his teeth had fallen out, he smoked and drank unstintedly, and in Antwerp had been diagnosed as a syphilitic (correctly or not is uncertain, he never confessed to receiving treatment). Theo worked for Goupil & Co, and in 1886 introduced him to the Impressionists and Neo-Impressionists, including Toulouse-Lautrec, a man who in society 'was conspicuous by his absinthe'.

Van Gogh's new friends told him to drop his dreary browns and umbers, to use plain bright colours and try the spotty technique of the 'confetti painter' Georges Seurat. He encountered Japanese woodcuts, which fascinated him. He did 200 paintings in two years, and a mural at the Café Tambourin. Hankering after a 'Studio of the South', he touched Theo for the fare to Arles (he sponged on Theo eternally, 'Thanks for your kind letter and the 50-fr. note it contained' is a repetitive theme in their correspondence). Arles boasts a Roman theatre and arena (still used for bullfights), and lies at the mouth of the Rhône amid the sunshine, soft smells and rosy walls of Provence. When he arrived on 20 February 1888, it was deep under snow.

Van Gogh booked into the Hôtel-Restaurant Carrell, moving after a row about the bill to the Café de la Gare, then he rented the dilapidated Yellow House. In October, he invited Gaugin to stay. They had 'temperamental incomparability', Gaugin discovered. On 23 December, his host suffered an attack of delirium, confusion and hallucinations, and threatened him with an open razor. Gaugin wisely left for a hotel, and van Gogh sliced off his own left ear lobe instead. He presented it at midnight to Rachel in the local brothel, with the invocation: 'Keep this object carefully.' Had she bottled it in spirit, God knows what it would have fetched today.

Van Gogh went home to bed, his ear bleeding profusely. He was found by the police on Christmas Eve and taken to Arles hospital, which he immortalised by painting. Forty curtained beds lined the long bare walls, its bare floor bore stout attentive nuns, and patients clustered in the corner round the iron stove with the gloomy ennui of today's round the ward television set. He was discharged early in January, and did his self-portrait, unwhiskered, ear bandaged, while he considered a papier mâché replacement.

A month later he was back, complaining of hearing voices and being poisoned by the citizens of Arles. He was drinking absinthe, also turpentine, and inhaling camphor, which he soaked into his bedclothes for sleep. The hospital locked him up, without tobacco, books or paint. He retained no memory of the symptoms which had brought him there. 'The overexcitement has been only temporary,' wrote Dr Felix Rey from the hospital cheerfully to Theo. 'I am firmly convinced that he will be himself again in a few days.'

Eighty citizens of Arles had petitioned the mayor to dispatch him to an asylum. But in May 1889, he forestalled them by entering the private asylum of Saint-Paul-de-Mausole, twenty-five kilometres away at St Rémy-de-Provence (birthplace of soothsayer Nostradamus). He felt that he could no longer cope with Arles. He had been there 444 days, with an outpouring of 200 paintings and 200 letters. He had his good days. 'I shouldn't be unhappy or discontented if some time from now I could enlist in the Foreign Legion for five years (they take men up to forty, I think),' he wrote to Theo. 'From the physical point of view my health is better than it used to be, and perhaps being in the army would do me more good than anything else.' *Beau Geste* would have been outshone.

At St Rémy he had a cell for sleep and a cell for work, and painted furiously. He stayed there a year, and had five relapses, generally after drinking outings to Arles (on one, he tried to down a quart of turpentine). He told Theo how these attacks of 'exhalta-tion or delirium' left him not knowing where he was, his mind wandered, he became twisted by enthusiasm, or madness, or prophecy, and they were followed by terrible fits of depression. But the asylum's Dr Peyron could make the note: 'His thoughts of suicide have disappeared, his appetite has returned, and he has resumed his usual mode of life.' Theo got two of his pictures into the Salon des Indépendents, where they puzzled everybody.

In May 1890, he felt well enough to quit the asylum, particularly as the nursing nuns in the adjoining cloisters were threatening him with 'perverted and frightful ideas about religion'. He moved north of Paris to Auvers-sur-Oise, lodging at the Café Ravoux (you can still get lunch there). He took instantly to Dr Paul Gachet, five minutes' walk away, a widower with a nineteen-year-old daughter, a pipe-smoker who robustly advised no smoking, no drinking, hard work and sound sleep.

Patient and doctor had an admirable relationship. 'I have seen Dr Gachet, who gives the impression of being rather eccentric, but his experience as a doctor must keep him balanced enough to combat the nervous trouble from which he certainly seems to me to be suffering at least as seriously as I,' van Gogh wrote to Theo. 'His house is full of black antiques, black, black, black, except for the impressionist pictures mentioned. When he spoke of Belgium and the days of the old painters, his grief-hardened face grew smiling again, and I really think I shall go on being friends with him and that I shall do his portrait.'

He depicted him Sitting at a Table with Books and a Glass with Sprigs of Foxglove, elf-faced with ginger hair and moustache, in a flat cap and a reefer jacket sitting on a purple couch, right hand supporting cheek-bone, looking worried about something. 'I painted Dr Gachet with an expression of melancholy, which would seem to look like a grimace to many who saw the canvas . . . I have found a true friend in Dr Gachet, something like another brother, so much do we resemble each other physically and also mentally. He is a very nervous man himself and very queer in his behaviour.'

Van Gogh had borrowed a pistol to scare off the crows while working outside. On Sunday 27 July 1890, he left the Café Ravoux with his painting gear and once out of sight shot himself behind a farm manure heap. He returned to the hotel, and went bleeding to bed in his whitewashed attic room with its skylight. 'Oh, nothing, I am wounded,' he called to the solicitous M Ravoux. They summoned Dr Gachet, who found the patient smoking his pipe. 'I shot myself. I only hope I haven't botched it. I will do it all over again,' he explained.

The doctor found a wound at the edge of the left ribs, in front of the line of the armpit. He concluded that the bullet had entered the pleural cavity and was lodged behind the heart. But the patient had no symptoms. The missile may have passed only through the superficial tissues and disappeared (the discovery of x-rays lay five years ahead). At one in the morning, two days later, van Gogh died suddenly in his brother's arms perhaps from haemorrhage, or delayed collapse of the lung, or from a heart attack. 'Well, my own work, I am risking my life for it and my reason has half foundered because of it—that's all right,' ended a letter to Theo found on him. Six months later, Theo was dead, too.

Van Gogh's mental diagnosis is as difficult to define as his cause of death.

1. *Self-poisoning.*

   Alcohol. 'The only thing to bring ease and distraction, in my case and other people's too, is to stun oneself with a lot of drinking or heavy smoking,' van Gogh had decided.

   Absinthe is an alcoholic drink laced with oil of wormwood, thujon, which can cause restlessness, giddiness, visual and auditory illusions, convulsions, paralysis, delirium and death. (A wormwood tree grew reprovingly over van Gogh's grave.)

   Turpentine causes vomiting and diarrhoea, excitement and muscular incoordination. It is drinkable: rectified oil of turpentine was at the time being prescribed for settling the stomach.

   Camphor causes excitement and convulsions.

   Lead. Van Gogh ate his paints, but he had no signs of chronic lead poisoning.

2. *Manic Depressive Illness*.

Dr Peyron at St Rémy diagnosed 'acute mania with hallucinations of sight and hearing which have caused him to mutilate himself by cutting off his ear'.

Hyperactivity, hallucinations, irritability, insomnia and bouts of drinking alternate in manic-depressive patients with gloom, loss of interest in life, a feeling of worthlessness and suicidal temptations. In between, they are normal. It is a familial disorder, and van Gogh's brothers Theo and Cor, who committed suicide aged twenty-three, and his sister Wil all had mental illness.

3. *Porphyria*.

Like George III. A hereditary disease of blood formation, bringing fits, hallucinations and emotional instability. But it causes also paralysis, disorders of touch, gripping abdominal pain, a rash and urine turning red, none of which van Gogh suffered.

4. *Epilepsy*.

Dr Peyron wrote: 'It is my opinion that M van Gogh is subject to epileptic fits at very infrequent intervals.' But he never suffered the characteristic seizures, with their preceding 'aura' described by Galen, and their succeeding 'tonic' and 'clonic' stages of spasm and convulsions.

5. *Syphilis*.

If van Gogh had contracted syphilis from Sien in The Hague in 1880, ten years later he could have been exhibiting the renowned delusions of grandeur, also dementia, mania, paranoia and depression, all colours of his clinical picture.

6. *Schizophrenia*.

The jerky lines and impatient dabs of *The Church at Auvers*, painted in 1890, the weird circles of *The Starry Night*, the convoluted *Cypresses* and *Trees in Front of the Entrance to the Asylum* of 1889, are magnificent examples of the mannerisms which encroach into the drawings of schizophrenics. Schizophrenics become, like van Gogh, withdrawn, paranoid, hallucinatory, murderous, self-mutilating (the ear-lobe, the hand in the lamp) and hyper-religious ('I have noticed again and again that lay interest in ecclesiastical matters is often a prelude to insanity,' Evelyn Waugh wrote later). But schizophrenics write as well as draw, turning out meaningless airy philosophical prose. Van Gogh's letters, of which 700 are still with us, were persistently practical:

Why do you say Degas is impotently flabby? (*he wrote to the painter Émile Bernard in July 1888*). Degas lives like a small lawyer and does not like women, for he knows that if he loved them and fucked them often, he, intellectually diseased, would become insipid as a painter.

Degas' painting is virile and impersonal for the very reason that he has resigned himself to be nothing personally but a small lawyer with a horror of going on a spree. He looks on while human animals, stronger than himself, get excited and fuck, and he paints them well, exactly because he doesn't have the pretension to get excited himself.

Rubens! Ah, that one! he was a handsome man and a good fucker, Courbet too. Their health permitted them to drink, eat, fuck. As for you, my poor dear comrade Bernard, I already told you in the spring: eat a lot, do your military exercises well, don't fuck too much; when you do this your painting will be all the more spermatic.

'Eccentricities of genius, Sam,' observed Mr Pickwick to Mr Weller about some oddities of medical students. There are the idiosyncratic illnesses of genius, too. The best diagnosis we can make of our artist is that he suffered from van Gogh's disease.

Van Gogh was a difficult patient for Dr Gachet. But in May 1990, the doctor's melancholy portrait was sold for a stupefying $82.5 million, $25.5 million more than the artist's previous top price. A pleasantly precise way of expressing appreciation of your medical attendant.

DOCTORS AND NURSES

$\mathscr{F}$LORENCE $\mathscr{N}$IGHTINGALE

1820–1910

ON 28 JULY 1856, two months after the Peace of Paris ended the pestiferous Crimean War, the most glorified female of her country since Queen Elizabeth I sailed from Constantinople in the steamer *Danube*, as Miss Smith. She appeared unexpectedly from the railway station at her family's Derbyshire home, a pale woman in a dull black dress with lace cuffs, after 632 days away at the war. She shortly moved south to fashionable Mayfair in London, where she went to bed, and stayed there until her death fifty-four years later.

Florence Nightingale was a hysteric.

The label seems an outrageous application to a woman who, had she and Lord Cardigan exchanged posts, would have immortalised the Charge of the Light Brigade as a resounding British victory.

Florence Nightingale became a nurse because God personally instructed her so, on 7 February 1837. God conversed with her four times later in life, though their relationship was an uneasy one: 'I MUST remember God is not my private secretary,' she was noting in the 1870s. Such inner voices are diagnostic of schizophrenia—sometimes urging their sufferers on to terrible things—but hysterics like Florence Nightingale, and her bellicose counterpart Joan of Arc, cheat a little by *saying* they have heard the word of God. This fortifies their shrewd manipulation, to their selfish advantage, of their fellow humans, to whom they present varying attitudes from utter helplessness and infuriating cussedness to illness and impending death.

Florence Nightingale's manipulations started on her family.

The Nightingales, like many rich English, were snobbish, arrogant and dotty. Father travelled constantly to relieve his pointless journey through life: Florence and her sister Parthenope—Greek for Naples—were labelled where they were born. The girls were presented to Queen Victoria and did the London season, taking half a floor at the Carlton Hotel. Florence grew tall, slim and charming, a clever letter-writer and a pleasant artist, but with an intelligence which bit and a wit which stung. Parthenope helped mother arrange the flowers.

At twenty-three, Florence turned dreamy, introspective, ruthlessly self-critical and bored, and declared that she would be a nurse. It was the year that Sara Gamp, gin and umbrella, hit the bookshops. Her intention provoked family disgust and terror in a deluge of sal volatile.

Florence could respectably have become a nursing nun, but such submissiveness to her valuable colleague God was unthinkable. She started as a deaconess in a blue print dress and little white cap at Kaiserswerth on the Rhine, in a Protestant institution part penitentiary, part asylum and part 100-bedded hospital, while the family took the waters at Carlsbad. Nursing is a mystic occupation which magnetises hysterics: but a flinty routine of rising at five, working until seven at night, with three breaks for gruel and broth, followed by Bible-readings until bedtime, proved a swift antidote to mysticism.

She was home in three months, reflating her mother with soaring marital ambitions. But Florence Nightingale was anyway a lesbian. At twenty-five, her cousin Henry Nicholson wanted to marry her. She fell for his sister Marianne instead: 'I never loved but one person with passion in my life and that was her,' she said, with the matter-of-factness which she applied to an appreciation of turpentine poultices.

Florence Nightingale's next manipulative victims were sick gentlewomen in distressed circumstances. God personally advised her to nurse them at No. 1 Harley Street, where she so effectively bossed the institution, cutting its costs in half, that when the Crimean War broke out in 1854 she had no trouble manipulating Sidney Herbert, the Secretary at war, to have the Cabinet appoint her to boss the venturesome nurses at the English Hospital in Turkey. The War had been a rapidly rising monument of incompetence for six months, with William Howard Russell reporting to *The Times* of medical care unelaborated since Waterloo, lacking surgeons, nurses, medicine and supplies, even rags to staunch the wounds.

She was the angel who rushed in where fools dared to tread. She arrived at the Scutari hospital synchronously with 1,050 casualties shipped from the Charge of the Light Brigade, crammed under their filthy greatcoats on deck, frostbitten, suffering dysentery and cholera, a dozen corpses a day tossed by the sailors into the Black Sea like dead horses.

Florence Nightingale 'was a shocking nurse,' disclosed Parthenope, from her own sickly experience. But the Sarah Gamps did the nursing. Miss Nightingale manipulated the administration and the politicking. 'Whereas her influence on people's minds and her curiosity in getting into varieties of minds is insatiable,' Parthenope added flatteringly or jealously. 'After she has got inside, they generally cease to have any interest for her.'

With £30,000 of *The Times*' money to spend in the Constantinople bazaars, Florence Nightingale could honestly claim to have started nursing the British army, then clothing it, feeding it, writing its letters home, making its wills and burying a good proportion of it (2,000 in her first winter). Had she later taken to politics instead of to bed, she would have been the first British female Prime Minister 125 years early.

Hysterical humans are incandescent in the limelight. They are the showmen, the actors, the overpowering salesmen, the revivalist preachers, the demagogues. 'Miss Nightingale now queens it with absolute power,' grumpily recognised one of the army doctors, whom she manipulated like a cook with a handful of wriggling eels for the stewpot. At night, she toured the four miles of whitewashed Scutari wards with her lamp (it was collapsible Turkish like a Chinese lantern, not the Aladdin's lamp of her London statue and legend). The patients supposedly kissed her dim shadow. It caught the imagination of the British public and of Longfellow:

A Lady with a Lamp shall stand
In the great history of the land,
A noble type of good,
Heroic womanhood.

Florence Nightingale glittered in every London paper from the *Spectator* to *Punch*. She was wafted from music-hall songs, embossed on greengrocers' bags, fired in vivid pottery, perpetuated as the name of streets and children, as a racehorse and in wax at Madame Tussaud's. Her anagram was discovered to be 'Flit on, Cheering Angel!' When she caught the deadly Crimean fever, alarm and anguish filled the cottages of England. No one else cared for the men in the ranks—except the Queen, who sent her a diamond broach saying *Blessed are the Merciful*, designed by Albert. Florence Nightingale was the heroine of the humble. She loved it.

Then the war was over. She thenceforth manipulated the British Empire.

Florence developed palpitations, rapid breathing, headaches and pain in the chest. She went to Malvern for the water cure, but it did not work. Her doctor asserted that her heart beat too fast, she must lie down and not get up until it was normal. This advice she obediently followed at the Burlington Hotel off Savile Row, next at 32 South Street off Park Lane (rent free). She was an invincibly pathetic invalid. Her weakness, her agonies, were continually manifested amid her pitiful laments, interrupted by her 'attacks' of panting and paralysis, which exploded among her entourage a panic of pillows, water, flying towels, sal volatile and brandy.

Florence Nightingale lived on a couch or in a wheel-chair, and if she steeled herself to travel commanded a special railway carriage. But why need she venture into the world, when the world came submissively to her? Viceroys, ministers, ambassadors and prelates appeared beseechingly at her bedside, also Jowett the omniscient Master of Balliol, who grew amorous. Equally usefully, people whom she did not want to see, like Mr Gladstone, could be blamelessly avoided by recurrent relapses. It was a brilliant performance of valetudinarian fraud.

She worked furiously: 'I am so busy that I have no time to die,' she complained. She masterminded the Royal Commission to reform the Army Medical Department. She organised the sanitation of India. She founded in 1860 the Nightingale Training School at St Thomas's Hospital, opposite the Houses of Parliament. She designed hospitals, down to the colours of the walls (she preferred pale pink), to the books in the library and where to carve the Sunday roast. 'It may seem a strange principle to enunciate as the very first requirement in a Hospital that it should do the sick no harm,' she noted, with her genius for rubbing noses into facts right in front of them. Though she refused to believe in germs, even when these had become as familiar to the world as houseflies.

Her fingers reached from her counterpane to every sickbed in the world. She wrote *Notes on Nursing* at 5 shillings, *Notes on Nursing for the Labouring-Classes* at sevenpence, also *Suggestions for Thought to the Searchers after Truth among the Artisans of England*, about which John Stuart Mill was most kind. Only immobility prevented her accepting an invitation to take charge of Lincoln's hospitals in the Civil War. She tried to reform the British War Office, but discovered it impregnable. She then developed backache, which she cured with implants of opium, which like many others she found allowed her pleasantly to forget herself for a while.

The resolutely pathetic make stern mistresses. Florence Nightingale refused to believe that everyone else was not shamming illness like herself. She compelled the help of Sidney Herbert, a man who could talk to ministers, ruining his salmon fishing. He became ill with chronic nephritis, for which she prescribed cotton soaked with chloroform and camphor; she was convinced that he was idling in bed, and was annoyed by his dying aged fifty.

Her two whipped curs from the bedside were the handsome Scottish doctor John Sutherland, a drains expert, who copied her manuscripts, and the poet Arthur Clough, who posted them and bought the groceries. Sutherland was deaf; she was certain that he feigned it to annoy her, and threatened to furnish him with an ear-trumpet. She summoned him with a loud bell and every day sent him impatient rude notes. He had given up a steady £1,500 a year from the Government to work with her, even on Sundays; he hardly saw his wife in his north London home, where she complained in bafflement that 'he always has some *pond* to dig in his garden'.

Once summoned from home late at night through teeming rain, Sutherland arrived in a temper which induced in his mistress a fit so severe that it filled him with transient alarm at precipitating her death. When he himself irritatingly died in 1891, his last words were 'gie her my love and blessing.' She was earlier annoyed with Clough deserting her to go to Italy and die in 1861, he possibly murmuring: 'Say not the struggle naught availeth, the labour and the wounds are vain.'

Florence Nightingale ended up fat and moon-faced, petting the young girls sent round from the St Thomas's Hospital Nursing School. With that delicacy of timing which distinguishes the British Government's distribution of its twinkling lustres, in 1907 she became the first woman to enjoy the Order of Merit. The next year, the City of London chipped in with its freedom. She died of heart-failure, rambling and mindless aged ninety, an age when even a hysteric is entitled to a fatal illness.

$\mathcal{S}$IGMUND $\mathcal{F}$REUD

1856–1939

AH, *fin de siècle* Vienna! *Gaieté Parisienne* erupting in middle Europe. The Parisian Opera House on the Ringstrasse, the Theatre an der Wien, the hums of Strauss, the jokes in *Die Fackel*, cafés, Tokay, electric trams, the blue Danube and the sylvan Prater, *Wiener Schnitzel* and *Sachertorte* and whipped cream with everything.

Freud was no Fledermaus. 'I dislike the faint mental obfuscation that even a slight drink induces,' he shuddered. Every Wednesday night, ten serious people gathered in his waiting-room to discuss the human mind. Over coffee. Not even a refreshing glass of young Gumpoldskirchen.To relax afterwards, they played a few hands of tarot.

These origins of psychiatry, though admirably sober, were scientifically lunatic.

Freud had been a straightforward neuropathologist, lecturing over pickled brains in glass bottles at the vast Vienna General Hospital, north of the Hofburg Palace. In the winter of 1885, he was invited to La Salpêtrière Hospital in Paris to attend the famed lectures of Jean-Martin Charcot, something of a clinical showman. He presented Freud with Mlle Deneuve, the twenty-two-year-old fiancée who joined the grotesque cast of medical history through her right-sided paralysis—to which she strangely expressed *la belle indifférence*—dramatically cured by Charcot's hypnosis, and ascribed to achieving postponement of her wedding to a man she did not love. It struck Freud then that there was more in the brain than met the dissector's eye.

In August 1891, Freud moved with his burgeoning family of four into No. 19 Berggasse, an address which has entered the world's awareness as deservedly as No. 221B Baker Street in London. The cobblestoned Berggasse—Hill Street—is near the General Hospital, sloping towards the Danube Canal in middle-class north Vienna. No. 19 is a massive building, grey-faced in concrete, its pair of stolid front doors enjoying the grandeur of arch and pediment, a courtyard in the rear with trees, its lowest level the local shops. The Freuds occupied a first floor flat of eighteen rooms, over the butcher's.

The varnished door from the staircase which presented the plate: 'Prof Dr Freud, 3–4'—admirably relaxed consulting hours—was reinforced inside with heavy iron bars against burglars. To the right of the tiny foyer was the waiting-room, which had a sofa, and led through double doors to the consulting-room, which contained The Couch, which was to become the delightfully exculpatory icon of the twentieth century.

People who meet regularly to discuss anything, from the political future of the world to keeping goldfish, tend to form themselves into societies. Freud's friends over coffee became the Psychological Wednesday Night Society, which with strengthening self-import-ance became in 1908 the Vienna Psychoanalytic Society, and in 1910 the International Psychoanalytic Association.

Drink is no less intoxicating then unrebuked enthusiasm. Like frisky Tyrolean chamois, they leapt from intellectual peak to peak, taking foothold on the slopes of Nietzsche and Schopenhauer to reach unexplored tracts of the human mind, many of which were heavily shrouded in cloud-cuckoo-land. Medicine, philosophy and fantasy created a *Weltanschauung*, which Freud rightly suspected 'the human rabble' might later not wholly appreciate. He gathered a secret clique to propagate his psychological inspirations, distributing among these acolytes Grecian rings like the one he wore himself: a ring, as they all knew, being the totem of erotic union.

Dreams and fancies were their symptoms, psychoanalysis their cure-all, as bleeding had been for the barber-surgeons. It is clearly comforting to spill your mentally flatulent beans to a professionally sympathetic listener, particularly when assured that their stinking antisocial effects are not your own fault. To deepen their vocational commitment, these pioneer psychiatrists all psychoanalysed each other. The predictable result was clinical chaos.

Among his coffee circle, to be analysed by Freud himself had the éclat of confessing directly to God. But who does God himself confess to? He may be superficially sinless, but once a psychiatrist gets to work on the divine psyche, who knows? Freud was thus a difficult psychiatric case, complicated by the appearance in Vienna of the woman in furs.

Lou Andreas-Salomé came from Germany in 1912. A strapping woman of queenly dominance, aged fifty-one, she sits lengthily coiled in fox-furs at Freud's right in the group photo. She had been the mistress of Nietzsche and Rilke, which must have improved her mind, if strained her equanimity. Her targets in Vienna were learning psychoanalysis and seducing Freud, for which she had awesomely prepared herself by reading through all his works.

Freud was soon sending her flowers, walking her home in the small hours, lecturing with his eyes magnetised by hers, or even by her vacant chair. 'Curiously enough without a trace of sexual attraction,' he protested, in the piffling spirit that confessed his indifference to alcohol. Freud was then dutifully psychoanalysing the psychoanalyst victor Tausk—a Croat, handsome, dashing, depressive, a womaniser and broke. Tausk overlooked Lou's eighteen-year seniority and allowed himself be seduced instead.

Absence of sexual attraction towards Lou did not spare Freud jealousy of Tausk, whom he anyway suspected of stealing his best ideas. But he did not interfere with the couple's professional relationship—Tausk was routinely psychoanalysing Lou—because Lou was for him a useful spy on the couch. This tacky tangle was snipped by the War, which conscripted Tausk as a medical officer. He survived, to implore more analysis by Freud, who rejected him but offered him analysis by young Helene Deutsch, whom Freud was inevitably psychoanalysing.

It appealed to Tausk to lie on Helene's couch six days a week, knowing that she would be lying on Freud's just as often. In this psychological *ménage à trois* Helene was meanwhile covertly psychoanalysing Freud. She had left her handbag on The Couch, a blatant sexual proposition: 'Something that is never absent, the patient's emotional transference on to her physician,' Freud murmured, in his dismissive alcohol-sexual mood.

Helene now fell for Tausk. When Freud demanded that she must choose between his psychoanalysing her and her psychoanalysing Tausk, she adhered to The Couch. Such complications were fatal. On 3 July 1919, Tausk drank a bottle of slivovitz, shot himself with his army revolver, and to make sure hanged himself as he fell to the floor with a rope secured round the bannisters. Freud wrote to Lou Andreas-Salomé: 'I confess I do not really miss him'.

Three years later, Herbert Silberer, of the waiting-room coffee-drinkers, had a row with Freud over the interpretation of dreams, received a rude letter—'I no longer desire personal contact with you'—and hanged himself from the bars of his hall window, arranging a flashlight so that his strangled face greeted his wife as she opened the front door from an evening out. Psychiatrists, like their patients, have their oddities.

In 1910, a psychopath of later renown was living meanly in a men's hostel at No. 27 Meldermannstrasse in Vienna: unshaven, lank-haired, in a secondhand bowler hat, dividing his days between reading politics in the Vienna public library and painting Viennese landmarks for sale in the furniture shops. When he returned to Vienna on 12 March 1938, he confronted Freud and most of his fellow analysts with extermination.

Anschluss Vienna destroyed the Psychoanalytical Association's library and arrested Freud's daughter Anna. But in Whitehall and Washington, Freud was a vague freak unworthy of diplomatic exertion. The more perceptive American ambassador in Paris nudged President Roosevelt, a ransom seeped into jackbooted trouser pockets, an *Unbedenklichkeitserklärung* in the summer of 1938 freed the Freuds to exile. Freud was first forced to attest that the Nazis had treated him with the respect, consideration and academic freedom worthy of a great scientist. He added: 'I can heartily recommend the Gestapo to anyone,' the admirable ultimate of his dismissive attitude to drink and sex.

Freud suffered from nasal catarrh (like Hitler), migraine, indigestion, constipation and moodiness. He was an incorrigible cigar-smoker, even beside The Couch—Helene Deutsch discovered him so bored with her confessions that he dozed off, dropped his Havana and burnt the carpet. In 1923, he consequently developed carcinoma of the palate, for which he suffered a false roof to his mouth and thirty-one operations (one of these was a vasectomy, to stimulate the rejuvenating hormones of the testis). Twenty days after the start of Hitler's war, Freud died from his long disease. Like Napoleon III, Handel, Conrad and Karl Marx, he chose to leave his bones in England's green and pleasant graveyards.

The

Common

People

$\mathcal{M}$ARTIN $\mathcal{L}$UTHER

1483–1546

THE LUTHERS were in copper. Hans Luther had been a farmer in the beautiful and ore-studded Harz Mountains, who turned to mining and prospered with three copper-smelting furnaces in the municipality of Mansfeld. Martin was born at nearby Eisleben on a November midnight: his mother remembered the church chimes as the baby slipped out. He grew into a fine voice, and achieved choral scholarship at Magdeburg Cathedral, forty miles north on the way to Berlin. He graduated in 1505 from the University of Erfurt (second out of seventeen), stayed on to study law, but he was hit by a thunderbolt and became a monk instead.

After five years in the Erfurt Augustine monastery, Luther transferred as Professor of Theology to the new University of Wittenberg in Saxony, and in 1525 married a young nun. This was all in order: they had shelved their vows of celibacy, Luther having discovered them not justified from the scriptures. They had six children, one becoming an eminent physician.

In 1511, Luther had been dispatched to Rome, which inaugurated an antagonism to the Roman Catholic Church. He was incensed by the lucrative trade of supplying indulgences to sinners for cash, in which the Dominican John Tetzel was his local salesman. The money was proclaimed to be for the rebuilding of St Peter's, which obviously came expensive; actually, it was to pay off the Archbishop of Mainz's debt to bankers Fuggers of Augsburg, raised to buy his extra sees of Magdeburg and Halberstadt. 'Grand rough old Martin Luther' wrote ninety-five theses against indulgences, denying the Pope had the right to forgive sins anyway, which on 31 October 1517 he nailed to the church door at Wittenberg Castle.

Fr Tetzel withdrew to Frankfurt-on-the-Oder, where he produced counter-theses and burnt Luther's. Luther's students at Wittenberg burnt Tetzel's. The smoke from this theological disputation by bonfire wafted up the nostrils of Pope Leo X, who summoned Luther to Rome. Luther instead attacked the papacy in general, invoking a Bull of Excommunication of forty-one theses, which in the inflammatory atmosphere he burnt before his supporters in Wittenberg.

Everyone in Germany was now becoming excited. The Emperor Charles V, protector and executor of the Pope, ordered the burning of Luther's books. 'Whenever they burn books, sooner or later they will burn human beings also,' foresaw Heine in 1823, a warning which remained valid in Germany until 10 May 1933, when Dr Goebbels ransacked the country's university libraries and ceremoniously burnt at nightfall mountains of books uncongenial to the Nazis.

Luther was a busy man—professor, pastor, philosopher, unceasing author and letter-writer. He ran the Reformation in his spare time. The Emperor summoned him to the Diet of Worms on the Rhine in April 1521. Luther told the Diet: 'I neither can nor will revoke anything, seeing that it is not safe or right to act against conscience. Here I stand. I can do no other. God help me. Amen.' He was benignly kidnapped by friends on his way home, and secluded safe from the faggots in the Elector of Saxony's Wartburg Castle, as a country gentleman, 'Junker Georg'.

Luther was unusually ascetic, even among monks. He fasted for days on end, his bones becoming countable through his skin, to achieve spiritual tranquillity. He suffered severely from gout, belying the widespread envious mockery that this straightforward metabolic disease is caused by gorging on beef and swilling in port. He had the Anglo-Germanic preoccupation with his bowels (a Frenchman's internal obsession is his liver). The inspiration of the Reformation is said to have come to him while sitting at stool. His letters are vibrant with accounts of his constipation, his purgatives and their effects. He suffered prolapsed piles and an anal fissure, a condition of painfulness to test a martyr.

In the summer of 1529, Luther was lucky to recover from an

attack of the sudden, deadly English sweating sickness Sudor Anglicus, which caused 'a grete swetyng and stinkyng, with redness of the face and body, and contynued thrust, with a grete hete and hedeche because of the fumes and venoms'. It first hit England after the battle of Bosworth, postponed Henry Vll's coronation, shut Oxford and paralysed London.

This was England's third and severest epidemic, exceptional in spreading to Northern Europe and exceptionally mortal: 'No one thought of his daily occupations, women filled the streets with lamentations and loud prayers, and funeral bells tolled day and night'. An attack lasted a day, death came within hours. The only cure attempted in desperation was China root, sarsaparillas. After another epidemic in 1551, it vanished.

Like Samuel Pepys in London 138 years later, Luther stood fast in the bubonic plague which had hit Wittenberg in 1527. The University had moved 100 miles away to Jena, but Luther stayed and opened his house as a hospital. He prepared the thoughtful pamphlet *Whether One may Flee from a Deadly Plague*, concluding that if one had a job to do one may not.

And like Pepys, Luther suffered from the stone. On 19 February 1537, he had urinary retention following an attack of severe renal colic with the passage of a small kidney stone. He had been suffering these attacks and passing small stones for eleven years. He was then at the little town of Schmalkalden, 150 miles south of Wittenberg beyond Leipzig, for a conference of Protestant princes. As the princes had all brought their physicians, these clustered round Luther giving him enemas, hot abdominal cloths and perineal massage, but without effect.

Luther was difficult about doctors. He recognised that they existed to heal the body as the theologian to heal the soul, but they were not so good at it. His later robust attitude, that he would eat what he liked and die when God willed, is sadly unfashionable today. Though he *did* grow rather fat.

After six days of urinary retention at Schmalkalden, Luther was developing signs of kidney failure and told the doctors that he was going to die. He pointed out that he was well in with God, and he knew it. He wanted to die at home. The doctors shook their heads, but obediently dispatched him in the Elector of Hesse's carriage, with several doctors.

After ten miles jolting wildly along the wintry roads, they pulled up for the night at the inn at Tambach, where Luther peed liberally. Next stop was Gotha, where he passed six stones, one bean-sized. He regularly passed more stones on the jerking fortnight reaching home. The inspirer of the Reformation had found a cure for the common contemporary disease of kidney stones, which does not seem to have been acted upon, to the detriment of the carriage trade.

Nine years later, Luther was on theological business at Eisleben, fifty miles from Wittenberg. It was where he was born to the midnight chimes. He again expressed the mortal desire to go home: 'I will now no longer tarry, but set myself to go to Wittenberg and there lay myself in a coffin and give the worms a fat doctor to feed on'. But at quarter-to-three the morning after next he dropped dead there from a myocardial infarct.

Martin! thou shouldst be living at this hour, as Wordsworth chided Milton. Economics is the solemn successor to theology. Only a resolute mystic like you could achieve Reformation of Europe's shameful indulgence, the Common Agricultural Policy, by voicing the same stout declaration to the Diet of Brussels.

$\mathcal{S}$AMUEL $\mathcal{P}$EPYS

1633–1703

PEPYS WAS A difficult case of lithotomy.

He was twenty-five, he had witnessed King Charles I's behead-ing, he was down from Magdalene, Cambridge, and had started work as Teller of the Receipt in the Exchequer, and he had been two years married to pretty, fifteen-year-old Elizabeth St Michel of St Martin-in-the-Fields, whom he had loved so much that it made him feel ill.

On 26 March 1658, he was cut for stone. The operation was performed at his cousin Mrs Turner's, the neighbour of his father, the tailor, in Salisbury Court, between Fleet Street and the Thames. Hospitals were for paupers, there were no private clinics, so you took your surgery to a friend's or to an inn.

Like Dickens, Pepys had suffered since childhood from attacks of renal colic. He had a family history of urinary calculi—mother, aunt, brother. At twenty, a kidney stone had slipped down his ureter and stayed in his bladder, provoking different symptoms: frequency, intermittent pissing, pain above the pubis and at the tip of the penis, which, 'growing insupportable I was delivered both of it and the stone by cutting'.

Pepys' lithotomist was fifty-year old Mr Thomas Hollyer, who operated upon the poor at St Bartholomew's Hospital in the City, and at St Thomas's Hospital, then between the 'Ship' and the 'King's Head' among the coaching inns crammed south of London Bridge. Hollyer could choose between the suprapubic incision developed by Pierre Franco of Provence in 1556, or take the perineal approach inaugurated by the Neapolitan sur-geon Mariano Santo de Barletta in 1535. The stone being large and long-standing, Pepys was in for the 'Marian operation', which was much feared.

Pepys lay on the edge of Mrs Turner's four-poster, his ankles tied to the posts (the 'lithotomy position', which persists in gynaecology). Somebody held his scrotum out of the way, and Hollyer made a three-inch fore-and-aft incision, two fingers' breadth to the left of the anus. This admitted him into the vesicorectal space, a direct approach to the bladder, which avoided—with skill—the prostate and the seminal vesicles. The bladder was incised, and in a flood of blood and urine a stone was removed the size of a tennis-ball. As Pepys began his diary on 1 January 1660, the prize operation note of surgical history stayed unwritten.

Anaesthesia was 188 years in the future, surgical antisepsis 207: lack of the first was terrifying, but of the second potentially murderous. The patient's courage, like the wounded soldier's, was mocked by the fatal infections that rampaged round surgical beds. That year, Hollyer had thirty lithotomy patients, who lived; the next, he had four, who died. He was using a new set of instruments, which perhaps took time to become sufficiently messy with blood and fragments of flesh to grow colonies of microbes; or perhaps the survivors were all lusty young men like Pepys. His patient mounted the stone in a tasteful box, in the spirit that women later turned their polished gall-stones into necklaces, and every March held a party (Mrs Turner invited) to commemorate so desirably forgettable an event.

Bladder stones have afflicted mankind since the times of the mummified Egyptians among us. Susruta the Hindu surgeon was boldly removing them in the fifth century AD, and as late as 1790 John Jones—author of the handy *Plain, Concise, Practical Remarks on the Treatment of Wounds and Fractures* in the American Revolution—was remembered for the operation in Benjamin Franklin's will. Today, they are rare. Their cause is still unsolved, though infection is a factor, and in Pepys' unwashed times everyone was teeming with germs.

Stones provided a comfortable living for Mr Hollyer, later Master of the Barber-Surgeons' Company, though lithotomists suffered a strange vocational isolation. The Hippocratic Oath demanded oddly: 'I will not cut, even for the stone, but I will leave such procedures to the practitioners of that craft.' Mr Hollyer's scruffier contemporaries were the itinerant cutters for stone who roamed Europe like the old French troubadours, but with more incentive to please their patrons. Pierre Franco, whose technique was thrusting a dagger-shaped knife into the patient's side, and working it up and down until the slit was big enough to grab the stone, warned: 'If we lithotomists have a mishap, we must run for our lives.'

Ancient medicine was always as perilous for the doctor as for the patient. When the Queen of Burgundy died of the plague in 580, the King executed her two physicians on her tomb. The eye surgeon who failed with the King of Bohemia's blindness in 1337 was hurled into the Oder to drown. In 1464, the King of Hungary offered a rich reward for cure of his arrow-wound, but for failure, death. These medieval principles interestingly persist today, when the successful doctor pockets his substantial fee, but the perpetrator of a clinical disaster is promptly poleaxed with a writ for damages.

Even Mr Hollyer's skill was imperfect. He cut the seminal vesicles behind the prostate and left his patient sterile, though as the world knows, not impotent. Ten years postoperatively Pepys was vigorously having it off with Deb Willet, his wife's companion (on £8 a year), who had looked in to comb his hair, when his wife walked in. Five years later, Pepys was suffering from conjunctivitis with 'great pain and water in my eyes', also pus in the urine and stinging micturition, with fever, sore swollen testicles and pain in the back. He fretted over his eyes, which he thought worn out by overwork, and becoming convinced that he was going blind abandoned his diary in May 1669.

This combination of symptoms was possibly Reiter's syndrome, a sexually transmitted condition named after the German physician Hans Reiter, born in 1881. How fascinating Pepys would have found it, that we suffer diseases to be discovered by doctors yet unborn.

A true Englishman, Pepys was obsessed with his bowels. Constipation so weighed upon him, its relief matched the beast of burden shedding its load, and the passage of copious wind raised his spirits like a trumpet-call. To achieve both, he became the slave of the enema and the purge.

> Anon, about 8 a-clock, my wife did give me a Clyster which Mr Hollyard directed, *viz.*, A pinte of strong ale, four ounces of Sugar, and two ounces of butter . . . and taking my usual wallnutt quantity of Electuary at my going into bed, I had about two stools in the night—and pissed well. Voided some wind.

Such were the movements of 12 October 1663.

Wren's dome and Pepys' diary are monuments to genius. In the intellectually free-and-easy seventeenth century, genius could spill where it fancied; in our century, specialisation has become the counterfeit of brilliance. Sir Christopher and Pepys were scientists, vanguard members of the Royal Society for Improving Natural Knowledge, which was founded at the end of the Civil War, with Isaac Newton its President in 1703.

Pepys got on the title page of Newton's *Philosophiae naturalis principia mathematica*, introducing gravity in 1686, because he happened then to be President. He had been elected a Fellow on 15 February 1665, when his operation had already directed his curiosity to the science of surgery. At eleven o'clock on 27 February 1663, he walked from his office to Chirurgeon's Hall in the City, to hear a pertinent lecture from the Reader of the Barber-Surgeons' Company:

> . . . upon the kidneys, ureters, and yard [*penis*], which was very fine; and his discourse being ended, we walked into the Hall, and there being great store of company, we had a fine dinner and good learned company, many Doctors of Physique, and we used with extraordinary great respect.

They drank King Charles II's health from the golden cup given by Henry VIII—who bestowed the Company's charter, Holbein's picture of the event being on the wall behind them—which had bells on it, for every drinker to ring by shaking if he had drained it. The Royal College of Surgeons still has the cup, and can continue to provide the facility.

After dinner Dr Scarborough took some of his friends, and I went along with them, to see the body alone, which we did, which was a lusty fellow, a seaman that was hanged for a robbery.

The Barber-Surgeons got four felons a year for dissection, warm from the gallows.

I did touch the body with my bare hand; it felt cold, but methought it was a very unpleasant sight . . . Thence we went into a private room where I perceive they prepare the bodies, and there were the kidneys, ureters, yard, stones and seminary vessels upon which he read to-day. And Dr Scarborough upon my desire and the company's did show very clearly the manner of the disease of the stone and the cutting and all other questions that I could think of, and the manner of the seed, how it comes into the yard, and how the water into the bladder.

On 30 November 1667, Pepys was dining in the Strand—a bad dinner, terrible service, a two hours' wait with his napkin open—when he met the first Englishman to have a blood transfusion. The experiment was inspired by the Royal Society and performed by Dr Edmund King and Dr Richard Lower, 'the prime physician of his time', a friend of Pepys and consultant to Pepys' navy, who had experimented at Oxford with blood transfusions between dogs. The idea was replacing bad blood, which caused illness, with fresh blood from any convenient source.

The human subject was thirty-two-year-old Arthur Coga, a Bachelor of Divinity at Cambridge, 'a man that is a little frantic . . . that is poor and a debauched man', who a week earlier had a minute's transfusion of sheep's blood, about a pint. The doctors had differed in foretelling the result: it might cool his overheated brain, it might have no effect whatever. Coga told Pepys:

. . . that he finds himself much better since, and as a new man. But he is cracked a little in his head, though he speaks very reasonably and very well. He had but 20s for his suffering it, and is to have the same again tried on him—the first sound man that ever had it tried on him in England, and but one that we hear of in France, which was a porter hired by the virtuosi.

Coga explained his motivation to be not the twenty shillings, but that *Sanguis ovis symbolicam quandam facultatem habet cum sanguine Christi; quia Christus est agnus Dei*—the blood of the sheep symbolises the power of the blood of Christ; because Christ is the Lamb of God. He lectured the Royal Society about it, also in Latin. Twelve days later, the doctors tried again, still harmlessly, and Arthur Coga disappeared to join the men, women, dogs, cats, rats, rabbits, guinea-pigs, mice, monkeys and fruit-flies in the frisky heaven of medical martyrdom.

Professor Jean Denys in Montpellier had already given a feverish boy of fifteen a pint of blood from the carotid artery of a lamb. His next transfused patient died, the widow won damages, the Faculty of Medicine of Paris regulated the practice, the French law forbade it, and blood transfusion vanished in England until Pepys had been dead 230 years.

The Great Plague of London would have been nothing without Pepys. The alternative diarist John Evelyn is perfunctory about it: he notes the empty streets, the shut shops, the mournful silence, the 'not knowing whose turn might be next', and the begging pestiferous poor from whom he seems to hurry away with his coat-collar turned up. Daniel Defoe's *Journal of the Plague Year* was published fifty-seven years afterwards, Defoe at the time of the Plague being but five. Only the weekly Bills of Mortality would have starkly told of 100,000 Londoners dead in the summer and autumn of 1665, had not Pepys' cheerful and curious eye observed the cadaverous pageant.

In that hot June of tolling bells and midnight funerals, Pepys saw in Drury Lane his first houses marked with a red cross and 'Lord have mercy upon us', with the plague sufferers incarcerated therein in pointless quarantine. He hurriedly bought some chewing-tobacco as a prophylactic. The next week, his hackney-coachman was stricken with the plague in the middle of Holborn. The next, he found everyone who could afford it—including the Court and most of the physicians—fleeing town in coaches and wagons. By October, he was observing:

> I walked to the Tower; but, Lord! how empty the streets are and melancholy, so many poor sick people in the streets and full of sores; and so many sad stories overheard as I walk, everybody talking of this dead and that man sick, and so many in this place, and so many in that. And they tell me that, in Westminster, there is never a physician and but one apothecary left, all being dead; but that there are great hopes of a great decrease this week: God send it!

Pepys lost only an aunt.

'I have never lived so merrily as I have done this plague-time,' he concluded that New Year's Eve. He had found plenty of good company 'and great store of dancings we have had at my cost (which I was willing to indulge myself and wife) at my lodgings'. That's the spirit! Two hundred and seventy-five years later, it helped a similarly perilous London through the blitz.

Disappointingly, Pepys' busy eye missed the plethora of dead rats. Black rats, killed by the fleas which injected man with the yet unknown *Pasteurella pestis*, had been noticed by lithotomist Susruta but by nobody since. The City fathers massacred the London dogs instead. Pepys perhaps survived the plague because he was unattractive to fleas. In the spring of 1662, he was put up by a surgeon in Portsmouth ('his wife a very pretty women'), sharing a bed with the Physician to the King's Household, and 'all the fleas came to him and not to me'. Pepys ascribed this to the doctor's bluer blood.

The summer after the blood transfusion, Dr Lower and Dr Turberville, Prince Rupert's oculist who treated Pepys, met Pepys in an ale-house in the Strand and took him 'to dissect several eyes of sheep and oxen, with great pleasure, and to my great information'. Dr Lower stayed a useful friend. Pepys unexpectedly found himself in prison, like another immortal, Mr Pickwick—with whom he shares an unflagging curiosity, a reflective mind, geniality, energy, cheerfulness, ebullience, level-headedness, an intense interest in fellow humans, the organisation of jollifications, and the dilution of this vale of tears with copious alcohol.

During the Popish Plot of 1679, when the Catholics were expected any moment to massacre the Protestants, burn down London and assassinate King Charles II, Pepys had been committed to the Tower for a couple of months on suspicion of treason. On 25 June 1690, when he was fifty-seven, he was suspected of being a Jacobite and imprisoned in Westminster Gatehouse beside the Abbey, which comprised the Bishop of London's prison for wicked parsons. Dr Richard Lower certified him as dangerously ill from a bladder ulcer, and got him out.

Seven years after his operation, Pepys had passed two kidney stones, with attacks of renal colic. Forty-two years after, his lithotomy scar broke down and leaked urine. He suffered fevers and severe bladder pain, feared to be caused by another stone. Perhaps he had an infected bladder cancer. He died at 3.47 in the morning of 26 May, in coma from hypertension caused by kidney-failure. He had the distinction of a post-mortem, which revealed seven stones impacted in his left kidney.

And so to bed, in his parish church St Olave's, near Tower Hill in the City of London. The original bladder calculus, sadly, joins the missing stones of Stonehenge as a vanished national monument.

$\mathcal{T}$YPHOID $\mathcal{M}$ARY

1869–1938

HOW DELIGHTFUL to escape the New York summer of 1906 to Oyster Bay, an old Colonial village with a natural harbour on the wooded north shore of Long Island, the home and the grave of Theodore Roosevelt. And how particularly agreeable to avoid the city's 3467 cases of typhoid fever that year, 639 of them fatal, annually shrugged off as unavoidable, like the hot weather.

Typhoid was accepted as the fault of bad water or bad milk, or rotting rubbish or the sewer gasses. It was exploding everywhere across America, particularly in the universities, which was of course the fault of the students. How the disease lay with its ticking fuse for years between unforeseeable epidemics was a mystery. Dr George A. Soper made a puzzled expedition that summer from New York City to Oyster Bay, where a household of ten had developed six cases (three of them servants). Typhoid was as unthinkable in Oyster Bay as poverty.

Dr Soper fell upon the water, the milk, the privy, the cesspool, the manure on the lawn, the neighbours, the menu. The case was solved! The family loved clams, provided by an old Indian woman on the beach, clearly their potential murderess. Her weapons would be the lively *Salmonella typhi*, the germs with flailing flagella cultured by Prussian army surgeon Georg Gaffky in 1884, and liable to lodge in clams. But not a clam had passed their back doorstep for six weeks, and typhoid strikes in a fortnight. Dr Soper had to think deeper.

Not a typhoid bug was detected by the frustrated Dr Soper in the urine and faeces of the four household survivors. Any visitors? he inquired. Well, the cook. Cook! Which cook? Oh, a Mary

Mallon from Ireland. Describe, please? A fat unmarried woman with thick greying hair and thick eyebrows and round steel-rimmed glasses, who had a surly mouth, was shy and secretive and silent about her past. She was a good cook as cooks go, and—as Saki had noticed—as cooks go she went, lasting from three weeks before the outbreak to three afterwards. She made the most *delicious* ice cream.

Dr Soper hastened to Mary's employment agency in the City. He could follow her instructively from stewpot to stewpot. In the summer of 1900, she had cooked in a rented house at Marnaroneck, across the Sound from Oyster Bay, where a young man visiting caught typhoid. During 1901, she served a family in New York City, and the laundress got typhoid at Christmas. In 1902, she went to Dark Harbor, Maine, cooking for nine at a lawyer's summer cottage. Typhoid struck in a fortnight, seven were attacked. Mary escaped infection, like the master of the house, who was immune from earlier typhoid. He gave her $50 above her wages for her unselfish extra duties at the sickbeds. In 1902, Mary spent nine months cooking for a family of four with seven servants at Sands Point on Long Island. The laundress caught typhoid in a week, three other servants in the next fortnight. The New York Health Department was alerted, and suggested insanitary servants' quarters, or an insanitary laundress.

It took Dr Soper six months to confront Mary. She was cooking in a Park Avenue apartment house, where two servants were suffering from typhoid and the owner's daughter was dead of it. She had gone from Oyster Bay to Tuxedo, NY, smiting a servant there in two weeks. Dr Soper explained to her patiently in the Park Avenue kitchen that she was unfortunately confirming the latest microbial theory: that the typhoid which so puzzled her as she shifted from job to job was spread by herself. She responded by attacking him with a kitchen cleaver.

He fled. The Health Department decided it must examine her. The police arrived at Park Avenue in force. Mary escaped, but was betrayed by a scrap of gingham trapped in an outside closet door, was besieged with ashcans, removed biting, screaming and kicking, and placed in a motor ambulance accompanied by an official from the Health Department, who was sitting on her chest. There were no typhoid bacilli in her urine, but her stools crawled with them like a hive with bees.

What to do with this legal mass murderess? Mary had been of utmost assistance to the entire medical profession by proving typhoid to be passed by immune carriers, but the doctors could hardly let her enthusiastically continue her valuable experiment. Particularly as the New York papers were depicting 'Typhoid Mary' as sizzling typhoid germs like hot dogs and grilling human skulls for breakfast. The Health Department isolated her for three years in the Riverside Hospital for infective diseases, on North Brother Island off the Bronx in the East River.

New York's monster was America's first identified typhoid carrier. She foreshadowed the discovery that, among patients recovering from the disease—perhaps from an attack so slight they were unaware of it—one in twenty continues excreting live germs for a year, some for life, nearly all of these women. Persons, not things, bring typhoid: they arrive in town and excrete their germs, then the water, the food, the milk and the flies carry them to the unsuspecting uninfected.

Dr Soper helpfully proposed to Mary the surgical removal of her gall-bladder, the typhoid reservoir, but she was so sullenly uncooperative he could have suggested beheading. Then give up cooking? But cooking was her living, her pride and joy! She resentfully felt herself the target of some doctors' plot, a conspiracy beyond her understanding, her victimisation beyond her reasoning. In 1910 she threw in the dishcloth. She promised never to shake another skillet, never to touch her fellow humans' food, and to report back every three months. They let her out and she disappeared.

It took the Health Department five years to trace her typhoidal spoor. A Mrs Mary Brown was cooking at the Sloane Hospital for Women in New York City, where twenty-five nurses had typhoid and two had died. The staff was laughingly calling her 'Typhoid Mary.' Mary vanished, was traced to Long Island, this time she came quietly, and returned to Riverside Hospital—for twenty-three years, all of them excreting typhoid bacilli. She mellowed. She changed sides, was appointed one of the hospital's laboratory technicians, and developed an interest in all medical conditions, except typhoid.

In 1923, the hospital built her a cottage, where she entertained favoured and brave members of the staff for tea. At Christmas in 1932 she was immobilised by a stroke. New York City could then list 290 known typhoid carriers. Mary missed being No. I for alphabetical reasons, but won immortality in the world's medical textbooks as No. 36. She died pious, but an unrepentant bacterial sinner, who never admitted being a carrier.

Mary Mallon was officially indicted with fifty-three cases and three deaths, but her casualty list was vastly more. She probably caused the 1903 epidemic at Ithaca, NY, with 1400 victims. She was buried in the Bronx, her funeral held at the spacious Roman Catholic Church of St Luke's, but only nine mourners came. Perhaps they were frightened of catching from such a perfectionist post-mortem typhoid.

FICTION

$\mathscr{L}$ADY $\mathscr{M}$ACBETH

1606

GLAMIS CASTLE in Angus overlooks the confluence of Dean Water and Glen Ogilvie, off the road from Perth to Forfar, which runs through the pretty and fertile valley of Strathmore, twelve miles north of the Firth of Tay and Dundee.

'This castle hath a pleasant seat,' observed King Duncan of Scotland approvingly, arriving in the middle of the night amid the flare of torches and the blare of hautboys. 'The air nimbly and sweetly recommends itself unto our gentle senses.'

His accompanying Thane Banquo noticed that the martlets loved it. 'No jutty, frieze, buttress, nor coign of vantage but this bird hath made his pendant bed and procreant cradle,' he pointed out, despite the pitch darkness. 'Where they most breed and haunt I have observed the air is delicate,' he added reassuringly to the man who ruled a land of granite hills, raw winds and bare knees.

They were interrupted by the appearance of their overnight hostess, Lady Macbeth.

Glamis Castle made a welcome stopover on the way to Inverness. It provided beds whereto a day's hard journey soundly invited, with adjacent accommodation for two chamberlains, cooking fit for banquets, and wine and wassail so freely flowing as to make memory a fume and reason a limbeck before inducing swinish sleep.

The castle was well staffed, with a sewer—he was the *maître d'hôtel*—divers servants, drummers, sennet sounders, a waiting gentlewoman and three murderers. The gate porter was lazy, surly, garrulous and competitively drunk and lecherous—he explained rudely to visitors how he could not physically be both at once—

forever grumbling that his job was like being the porter of hell-gate, except that the place was too cold for hell. There was also a resident doctor.

The doctor of physic was short, fat, neatly bearded, costumed in black doublet and hose. He was the personal attendant of Lady Macbeth, who had recently been causing him concern. She had revealed during a consultation an alarming desire for the spirits to 'Unsex me here, and fill me from the crown to the toe top-full of direct cruelty'.

Smoothing his lace collar, the doctor had murmured that such notions arise from the sex act, when the male inserts his penis aggressively—begging the Thane of Glamis' pardon—into the submissive female, who may yearn for compensatory dominance and the infliction of pain.

'I have given suck,' she interrupted fiercely, 'and know how tender 'tis to love the babe that milks me. I would, while it was smiling in my face, have plucked my nipple from his boneless gums and dashed the brains out.'

'Quite so,' the physician agreed. 'Bring forth men-children only, for thy undaunted mettle should compose nothing but males,' he advised.

Weird things were happening in Glamis Castle, the doctor was shortly to reflect. The King of Scotland had been spending the night, but early next morning Macduff, the Thane of Fyfe, was knocking at the gate, rousing the uncivil porter, then running about disturbing everybody by shouting: 'O horror, horror, horror! Awake, awake! Ring the alarum bell. Murder and treason!'

The King had been murdered. The chamberlains did it.

The pair of retainers was found unmannerly breeched with gore, bloody daggers lying unwiped on their pillows. Lady Macbeth was dreadfully upset.

'Help me hence, ho!' she groaned, clutching her woman's breasts, in which the milk was liable to turn to gall.

'Look to the lady,' directed Macduff gallantly.

'Look to the lady,' reinforced Banquo, chivalrously distracted from this most bloody piece of work.

Lady Macbeth left, attended.

The doctor recalled, puzzled, that she had asked him the previous evening for some drugs suitable for the chamberlains' possets, as she wanted them to get a sound night's sleep.

Then she had started suddenly, and cried: 'Hark, peace!—It was the owl that shrieked, the fatal bellman.' She had been at the wassail, too. She had confided in him carelessly: 'That which had made them drunk hath made me bold.' But everyone in the Castle that night had been wassailed out of their minds.

The political situation at Glamis was confusing, the doctor later pondered. Macbeth had recently become the Thane of Cawdor— which was miles up north, near gloomy Loch Ness—in reward for ousting some Norwegian hooligans arriving by Viking longship. Duncan's body had been removed to the sacred storehouse of his predecessors and guardian of their bones at Clomekill. Because of this inhospitable fatality, Macbeth was already on his way to Scone, twenty miles away near Perth, to sit on its stone and be invested as King of Scotland. Events were flying thicker and faster than the August grouse. Lady Macbeth was loving it.

As Banquo was still staying with them, the Macbeths gave him a little surprise.

'Tonight we hold a solemn supper, sir,' Macbeth twinkled at him. 'And I'll request your presence.'

Banquo said he would be delighted.

'Ride you this afternoon?' Macbeth asked offhandedly.

'Ay, my good lord,' Banquo nodded.

'Is't far you ride?' Macbeth inquired, absently flicking bap crumbs off his kilt.

'As far, my lord, as will fill up the time 'twixt this and supper.' Banquo glanced through the casement. 'I must become a borrower of the night for a dark hour or twain.'

'Fail not our feast,' smiled Macbeth.

'My lord, I will not,' he assured them happily.

Lord and Lady Macbeth's fingertips waved him good-bye.

The banquet was a disaster.

Lady Macbeth was queening it. Macbeth was heartily playing the jovial host. He was just inviting: 'Anon we'll drink a measure the table round,' when he was called to the door by a man with blood on his face.

He returned, apologising for the late Banquo. 'Now good digestion wait on appetite,' he invited, rubbing his hands.

'Mayn't please your highness sit?' suggested one of the thanes who crammed the groaning board.

'The table's full,' Macbeth indicated.

'Here's a place reserved sir,' the thane pointed out.

'Where?'

'Here, my good lord,' the thane replied unbelievingly. 'What is't that moves your highness?'

Macbeth jumped up. It was a joke in deplorable taste. 'Which of you have done this?'

They were baffled. 'What, my good lord?'

Macbeth screeched at his empty chair: 'Never shake thy gory locks at me.'

'Gentlemen, rise. His highness is not well,' urged the thane nervously.

'Sit, worthy friends.' Lady Macbeth was on her feet. 'My lord is often thus, and hath been from his youth,' she passed off the little peculiarity, saying it went away if nobody took any notice.

'Give me some wine. Fill full,' Macbeth wisely ordered from an attendant.

Everybody wassailed. But Macbeth got another nasty turn. He was shouting at his empty chair: 'Hence, horrible shadow, unreal mock'ry, hence!'

Lady Macbeth abruptly decided that the party was over.

The doctor was growing concerned about Macbeth. He was seeing things: a dagger, which he wondered distractedly was 'But a dagger of the mind, a false creation proceeding from the heat-oppressed brain?' And three weird sisters out on the blasted heath, giving him the daily horoscope. 'I am cabined, cribbed, confined,' the patient told him nervously. A clear case of hallucinatory claustrophobia.

They found Banquo biding in a ditch, with twenty trenchèd gashes on his head. The doctor shivered. People were already murmuring that Macbeth had done for Duncan. But he suspected that Macbeth was a man of flaws and starts, impostors to true fear: Lady Macbeth herself had complained his nature was too full o' th' milk of human kindness. She had once commanded: 'Hie thee hither, that I may pour my spirits in thine ear and chastise with the valour of my tongue all that impedes thee from the golden round which fate and metaphysical aid doth seem to have thee crowned withal.' After that outburst, that he lay in her power was as plain as the cat i' th' adage.

The doctor of physic was keen on the waiting-gentlewoman. After the day's work they would have a quiet wassail together. One night, Lady Macbeth appeared from her bedchamber in her nightie, with a taper. The doctor asked, did she often do this sort of thing?

'I have seen her rise from her bed, unlock her closet, take forth paper, fold it, write upon't, read it, afterwards seal it, and again return to bed, yet all this while in a most fast sleep,' the waiting-gentlewoman informed him.

'In this slumbery agitation besides her walking and other actual performances, what at any time have you heard her say?'

'That, sir, which I will not report after her.'

'You may to me,' the doctor told her pompously. 'And 'tis most meet you should.'

'Neither to you nor anyone, having no witness to confirm my speech,' she told him primly.

Lady Macbeth stood dryly washing her hands, despite holding a burning taper.

'I have known her continue in this a quarter of an hour,' the waiting-gentlewoman added.

Hand-washing rituals are indicative of an obsessional personality, the doctor diagnosed to himself with satisfaction.

The sleepwalker rambled irritably of damned spots, the smell of blood and the lousy perfumes of Arabia. She gave a deep sigh. 'What's done cannot be undone,' she concluded philosophically. 'To bed, to bed, to bed . . .'

'Infected minds to their deaf pillows will discharge their secrets,' the doctor pronounced weightily as she made her exit. He meditated that someone might usefully make a study of dreams one day. 'Look after her.'

'Good night, good doctor,' said the waiting-gentlewoman. She gave him a gentlewomanly kiss.

Macbeth was away at the time, down south in Fyfe, murdering Macduff's family. When Macbeth finally had the opportunity to ask: 'How does your patient, doctor?' ten thousand armed Englishmen had arrived outside and Macbeth was putting on his armour.

The doctor said frankly: 'Not so sick, my lord, as she is troubled with thick-coming fancies that keep her from her rest.'

'Cure her of that,' Macbeth commanded brusquely, buckling his breastplate. 'Canst thou not minister to a mind diseased, pluck from the memory a rooted sorrow, raze out the written troubles of the brain, and with some sweet oblivious antidote cleanse the fraught bosom of that perilous stuff which weighs upon her heart?'

Good idea, that, mused the doctor, stroking his beard. Use the past to cure the present. He suggested a tranquillizing draught.

'Throw physic to the dogs; I'll none of it,' decided Macbeth angrily, hastily pulling on his vambrace, but it did not fit. 'Pull't off, I say,' he commanded the attendant, adding bitterly to the doctor: 'What rhubarb, cyme, or what purgative drug would scour these English hence?'

They were interrupted by the news that his patient Lady Macbeth had died.

Macbeth took it well. 'All our yesterdays have lighted fools the way to dusty death,' he grumbled, adjusting his tassel.

Glancing through the casement, the doctor noticed that the surrounding woodland was moving. He felt the need for air. He escaped to the battlements, to be pursued by Macbeth, who was pursued by Macduff, claymore aloft.

'I bear a charmèd life, which must not yield to one of woman born,' Macbeth was shouting.

The doctor had to interrupt that he used to go out in Edinburgh with the midwife who was to deliver Macduff, but obstetrical complications arose and they had to do a Caesarean.

'Accursèd be the tongue that tells me so,' yelled Macbeth, swirling his claymore.

The doctor tightly shut his eyes. When he opened them, Macduff was holding Macbeth's dripping head. The doctor's well-paid job seemed to be finished. He was not sorry. 'Profit again would hardly draw me here,' he reflected sombrely. But it had all been interesting. Even dramatic.

ℬARON ℳUNCHAUSEN

1720–1791

Heironymus Karl Friedrich, Freiherr von Munchausen, lived at Bodenwerder on the River Weser, thirty miles south of Hanover, just past the Pied Piper's playground of Hamelin. In 1739, the Treaty of Belgrade ended a Turkish-Russian war, fought over grievances of incomprehensible complexity. The Baron had gone into battle as a German cavalry officer attached to the Russian army, and was home with many a tale to tell. Some of these glorious adventures against the menace of Islam, his friends came to admit, were a bit much.

In the imagination of the artist Gustave Doré, the Baron was a man of rough-hewn features, with a fierce hawk nose, sabre-pointed chin, bushy upswept moustache, a cheerful mouth, three horizontal ringlets against each temple, and squashed, deep eyes which were clearly proof against the pulling-over of any wool. His incredible exploits reached the ears of fellow Hanoverian Rudolf Erich Raspe, who knew the Baron when himself a student in Gottingen. In 1775, Raspe was exiled in London: he was Keeper of the Landgrave of Hesse's gems, but he sold them. He later discovered rich veins of gold on an English nobleman's estate, but as he had planted the samples himself, soon needed to proceed to Ireland, where he died in 1794.

Broke in London in 1785, Raspe wrote anonymously *Baron Munchausen's Narrative of his Marvellous Travels and Campaigns in Russia*, forty-nine pages at a shilling, an instant seller. A second edition appeared the next year from Oxford, then an enlarged one (illustrated), titled grandly *Gulliver Reviv'd*, and promising additionally the Baron's *Singular Voyages and Sporting Adventures as he relates them over a bottle when surrounded by his friends.* Like any ghost-writer, Raspe conscientiously exaggerated the performances of his hero. Baron Munchausen became a fairy-tale character, like that merry old soul King Cole. The book evolved into a miscellany of the laughably improbable, from the classics to the balloonists. Nobody knew that Raspe had written it until 1824.

One of the Baron's experiences:

Night and darkness overtook me. No village was to be seen. The country was covered with snow, and I was unacquainted with the road. Tired, I alighted, and fastened my horse to something like a pointed stump of a tree, which appeared above the snow; for the sake of safety I placed my pistols under my arm, and laid down on the snow, where I slept so soundly that I did not open my eyes till full daylight. It is not easy to conceive my astonishment to find myself in the midst of a village, lying in a churchyard; nor was my horse to be seen, but soon after I heard him neigh somewhere above me. On looking upwards I beheld him hanging by his bridle to the weather-cock of the steeple.

Matters were now very plain to me: the village had been covered with snow overnight; a sudden change of weather had taken place; I had sunk down to the churchyard whilst asleep, gently, and in the same proportion as the snow had melted away; and what in the dark I had taken to be the stump of a little tree, appearing above the snow, and to which I tied my horse, proved to have been the cross or weathercock of the steeple.

In 1951, the London physician Richard Asher discovered Baron Munchausen to be the cause of many difficult patients. These sufferers pass their lives touring hospitals with bizarre conditions, which reliably lead to their admission and often to exploratory operations. Dr Asher scientifically divided cases of Munchausen's syndrome into three types:

(1) Abdominal (laparotomophilia migrans). The patient travels the country enjoying operations in assorted hospitals, from which he spectacularly and prematurely discharges himself, even with oozing wounds and dripping drips.

(2) Bleeding (haemorrhagica histrionica). The patient appears at the hospital bleeding alarmingly, internally or externally.

(3) Neurological (neurologica diabolica). The patient has fits, dizzy spells, fainting turns, numbness, all of a peculiar sort, but all convincing and demanding investigation.

An aid to diagnosis was pockets stuffed with hospital attendance cards, insurance claim forms, and litigious letters, and an evasive and truculent manner.

The typical Munchausen patient arrives in the accident and emergency department in the middle of the night, desperately ill. His belly is crisscrossed with scars (the 'hot cross bun abdomen'). His medical history is a well-rehearsed interweave of fact and fiction. On admission, he is the perfect patient, ingratiating himself with the staff and requesting the hospital chaplain, tolerant of the most tormenting investigations. He departs like a quarrelsome overcharged hotel guest.

Typical Munchausen cases:

(1) A man habitually found lying in a pool of blood outside an assortment of English and Irish hospitals explained that he was a novice monk travelling to his monastery. The holy man disclosed that he bled readily from all bodily orifices, adding that his stepbrother was a case of Christmas disease—a rare form of hereditary haemophilia. This interested the haematology department, who busily applied their tests to a vagrant enjoying comprehensive hospital hospitality, while discretely scratching the inside of his nose for more blood to smear on his eyes and ears, and to spike his urine sample. (Haematuria can be produced by any convenient prong—eg, the wire round your hospital flowers—pushed up the

penis; haematemesis is mimicked by drinking pig's blood and vomiting on the reception hall floor.)

(2) A young woman appeared at a small London suburban hospital in alarm at swallowing two open safety-pins, held in her teeth while dressmaking. This was confirmed on x-ray. The surgeon who opened her stomach to remove them was also on the staff of a grand London teaching hospital, where he later urgently took over the operating-list of a sick colleague. He found with surprise that his anaesthetised first case was for swallowed safety-pins. It was the same patient, gone upmarket. The surgeon helpfully suggested that Munchausen cases have their photographs circulated to hospitals, like those of chronic drunks to publicans under the ancient Inebriates Act.

(3) In 1986, a thirty-two-year-old nurse, now living with her Siamese cats in Blackpool, concocted seven ectopic pregnancies. The inside of her pelvis became so blocked with adhesions from interference by the keyhole insertion of laparoscopes, the gynaecologists were obliged to open her up. This was her desire. In childhood, she had swallowed salt water to make herself sick, then complained of right-sided pain, and was rushed to the nearest hospital for an appendicectomy. Encouraged by her mother, who enjoyed the fun, by sixteen she had been admitted to hospital 200 times with various diseases, known and unknown, which were achieved either by stopping drinking for several days, by pushing a school rubber up her nose or by banging her knees with a hammer. Such love of hospitals inspired her to be a nurse; she now banged her head with the hammer, too, to substitute being nursed for nursing.

The British National Health Service, founded on the noble, if ludicrously impractical, principle of prompt and full free treatment for all, is a benevolent patron of the Munchausen sufferer. But the businesslike United States had discovered the 'professional hospital bum' by the mid-1950s.

(4) A young man in Virginia with an allergy to a skin remedy covered himself with it all over, causing a severe dermatitis which admitted him to the foremost Virginia and West Virginia hospitals, until they found a bottle of it in the case under his bed.

(5) In the summer of 1954, a thirty-nine-year-old professional wrestler burst by night into the emergency room of the University of Iowa Hospital, heavily spattered with blood. After intense investigation—of which he showed an uncanny foreknowledge—he was offered an operation on the abdominal veins, which he forcefully refused. He was equally suspiciously familiar with ward routine. He complained violently at any delay in his sedative injections, he threatened bodily harm to the staff, he intruded into the doctors' rooms loudly demanding a cure, and was reasonably described in his case-notes as 'obese, obtuse, obstinate, obstreperous, and obscene'. As he had earlier been a merchant seaman, he had sailed his syndrome round the world, scars on his back recording investigation of his kidneys in Yokohama.

When he started breaking up the ward and inflicting bloody wounds on his own legs, they tried getting rid of him to Chicago. But he returned in imploring tears, and kindly Iowa Hospital let him in again. Painstaking research by the hospital later disclosed that the wrestler had hitch-hiked round the United States and Canada to display the same symptoms, and the same reaction to treatment, in San Francisco, Chicago, Ontario, Newark, Louisville, Louisiana, Albany, Cleveland, Los Angeles, Detroit, Salt Lake City (where he leapt from the operating table while receiving a spinal anaesthetic, to leave the theatre in a toga of surgical towels, with a needle dripping spinal fluid from his back), Montana, South Dakota, Illinois, Milwaukee, Madison, Denver, Buffalo and finally Syracuse, whence he was not seen again and, to the relief of his doctors, had probably solved his case the only possible way, by dying.

The Munchausen syndrome is unique in striking by proxy. The mother induces signs of an illness, or an illness, in her child, and sits enjoying the loving attention. Worse, was the English nurse

Beverly Allitt: she killed four children in her hospital, to savour the drama.

Its causes—beyond the understandable ones of drugs, evading the police and free lodging—are:

(1) Playing the lead in the drama. Bernard Shaw lectured these therapeutic thespians in the preface to his play *The Doctor's Dilemma*, in 1911:

> There are men and women whom the operating table seems to fascinate: half-alive people who through vanity, or hypochondria, or a craving to be the constant objects of anxious attention or what not, lose such feeble sense as they ever had of the value of their own organs and limbs. They seem to care as little for mutilation as lobsters or lizards, which at least have the excuse that they grow new claws and new tails if they lose the old ones.

(2) Money. Commonplace today, but Shaw quotes the case of a man who laid on the line to let the London express amputate his legs so he could claim a pension.

(3) A grudge against doctors.

(4) Masochism, hysteria, schizophrenia and suchlike.

(5) The need for sympathy. The Munchausen syndrome is becoming commoner, and more varied, with the vastly increasing number of lonely and rootless people. How precious an organ, the sympathetic ear! Some sufferers recount imaginary dramatic bereavements to attract it—their beloveds in road accidents, dying in their arms. The professional, coddling care of a hospital can be discovered nowhere else. Elizabeth Barrett Browning discerned this in 1857:

> I think it frets the saints in heaven to see
> How many desolate creatures on the earth

Have learnt the simple dues of fellowship
And social comfort, in a hospital

The medical profession does not suffer the Munchausen syndrome. For any doctor, to find himself a patient is as devastating a reversal of roles as any colonel finding himself a prisoner of war. And any hospital, he feels inwardly, should be shunned as shiveringly as King Lear in the storm shunned self-pity—'O, that way madness lies'.